MECHANIX ILLUSTRATED
HOW-TO-DO-IT
ENCYCLOPEDIA

Edited by the Combined Staffs of MECHANIX ILLUSTRATED
FAWCETT BOOKS and ELECTRONICS ILLUSTRATED

IN SIXTEEN VOLUMES

VOLUME 12

COMPLETE CONTENTS
AND INDEX IN VOLUME 16

Well-known reader services of Mechanix Illustrated are extended to readers of this encyclopedia to the extent of blueprint and plan offerings as indicated throughout the various volumes. Inquiries relating to such services and communications regarding the editorial material in this encyclopedia should be directed to Fawcett Publications, Inc., Encyclopedia Service, 67 West 44th Street, New York 36, N. Y. Printed in the United States of America.

GOLDEN PRESS • NEW YORK

Planning the Darkroom

An orderly darkroom is essential for turning out good negatives and fine prints. Plan your working space to meet maximum needs.

YOUR DARKROOM planning should be well started before you look at equipment prices in the catalogues and camera stores. Just as you selected your one or more cameras to enable you to shoot certain types of pictures, design your darkroom with much the same kind of thinking: Line up your cameras on a desk and make a list of what you expect from each.

Say, for example, that you have a 35mm camera but you use this exclusively for color slides. Then you won't need 35mm film developing reels, a 35mm negative carrier for your enlarger, or the special 3-inch condenser for this negative size that an enlarger such as the Omega requires. The next camera, say, is a twin-lens reflex, and it is with this camera that you generally shoot the bulk of your black-and-whites. Then there's the 4x5 you used for several years—true, you don't have it anymore, but you do have a large collection of 4x5 negatives subject to future printing. So you decide that you'll need an enlarger that is capable of handling 2¼x2¼ and 4x5 negatives, and preferably one that can handle some 35mm if the occasion should arise.

Next, ask yourself if your darkroom efforts will be mostly toward the production of large 11x14's for contests and salons. Or will you standardize on 5x7's, which are less costly to produce and to distribute (for free) among the relatives? Will most of your work be 8x10's because you shoot weddings and this is the currently popular size for album presentations? Whatever the answers that come up, you'll have taken a step toward a better darkroom. As a result of this probing, you'll know in your own mind what you intend to do.

Where do you establish your darkroom? This is another of those self-questioning affairs. First, where will you be able to have a source of running water, preferably both hot and cold? The hot will be useful the year around in mixing chemicals, and in the winter for bringing up the temperature of the cold tap water (which in the northern states runs as low as 40 degrees). Cold water will be useful year around for washing prints, cooling developers to 68-70 degrees working temperature, rinsing trays, diluting old developers into the drain, etc.

In selecting the site for a home darkroom you are limited to what is available spacewise. Is there a basement? Take it in preference to an attic, which will require insulation from heat and likely some plumbing to bring in running water. Is there a spare room upstairs or on the main floor? Take that so that you can still be a member of the family, and your wife won't think she's a darkroom widow. Better yet, figure her into the deal: lay out your darkroom so that two can work in it. This doesn't mean two enlargers, but merely that while you expose the prints and oversee time and the tone progress of the print, your wife does the developing —then you'll be able to turn out a large number of prints in an evening and have somebody to talk to as well. A radio or record player also will add a lot to your enjoyment of an evening in the darkroom.

If you have a whole basement don't take half of it for a darkroom, but rather start out with an area about 6x10 feet. You can save construction of two darkroom walls in a basement by selecting a corner; paint the concrete so that it'll be easier to keep clean and will reflect more safelight illumination. Too large a darkroom can create extra steps, backtracking, and general wear-and-tear on the photographer. This will reduce both output and enjoyment. A basement darkroom will be vastly improved through the addition of a wooden floor section over the area where you do most of your standing.

Water was mentioned first before because it is easier to darken a room that has running water than to bring running water into a room that happens to be naturally dark. Many years ago it was the popular notion that a darkroom had to have every wall painted flat black. The

Ideal arrangement is to have what you are using regularly within easy reach and in good supply. While photographic supplies are not exactly cheap, they certainly are less valuable than time is—and time is the element you need most to produce better negatives and prints. The darkroom setups shown at left and above are only two of many, many possible ones.

modern idea is that a darkroom should be light (in color) but light-tight. Actually, there are very few times that you'll require total darkness—for instance, when loading film into hangers and reels for developing, loading black-and-white or color film into holders, loading bulk 35mm film into cartridges, and when duplicating color slides in black-and-white. The rest of your darkroom work will be under proper safelights or even in white light, and black walls would only absorb the light from the safelights. Light walls will make a small closet darkroom seem larger and more pleasant to work in. If you use a gloss-finish paint you'll be able to profit from an occasional washing to eliminate the brew of hypo and developer smells which cling to walls.

How dark is dark? A window—plus daylight-saving time during the summer—can mean an awfully late-at-night start on film developing unless you plan your darkroom right. Blankets are okeh for itinerant photographers who have to load holders in hotel rooms, but they aren't the answer for the home darkroom. Take the cost of blanket plus the regular laundry bills to remove the smells of photo solutions, and you'll realize that it's cheaper to have a snug-fitting piece of plywood cut for the window. Nicer yet is a light-tight shade which works on a pull string. The ultimate is a plastic blackout venetian blind (made by Victory Plastics Co. in Hudson, Mass.) which shuts out the light but not the fresh air. Weatherstripping may be necessary to seal out light from the inside halls and rooms.

We still want to know how dark is dark, so go into the darkroom and close the door (which has a sliding bolt in preference to a screen hook, since a hook won't hold the door as tight). Stand there for at least five minutes with the lights off. It will take this long for your eyes to become accustomed to the darkness. If it still looks dark, it's safe. It's an eerie feeling to be loading film onto reels in a "darkroom" and, by the time you get to the fifth reel, suddenly to realize that you can see your own hands doing it; light was there from the start, of course, but your eyes didn't see it. It is a good policy to make this five-minute test whenever you develop in somebody else's darkroom, no matter what they assure you.

So far, we have water and we have darkness; next comes efficient layout. Note that if you are right-handed, you'll find it smoother to work from right to left; if left-handed, from left to right. When you design a working shelf don't go by the dimensions you happen to read in a magazine plan. A 36-inch high shelf will be too high and too tiring if you are five-foot-four, while a 30-inch high working surface will be too low if you are a six-footer.

Omega 11x14 easel has firm paper grip, adjustable borders, large figures readable by lens light.

Airequipt easel is two-sided: shown is side for 5x7, 4x5, 2¼x3¼. Reverse handles 8x10-inch prints.

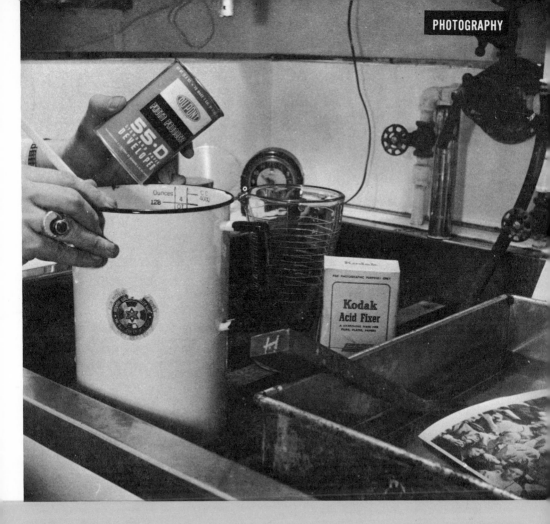

Packaged chemicals save a lot of time and money for individual darkroom worker. Many sizes are available, to fit your need. Mixing your own developers can be interesting—so can repairing your own shoes.

Allow enough space atop the work area for three of the largest print trays you might be using. Since 16x20 is the largest size that sheet enlarging paper comes in, this would be a good stopping place. (Beyond 16x20 you'll have to buy your paper in rolls, and the cost of a roll will more than equal the price of one or two prints made commercially at a photo-mural studio, without even considering the added cost of larger-than-16x20 trays.)

Ventilation is another important consideration. The simplest way to ventilate is to buy one or two lightproof fans specially made for photography. One is placed to carry the old air out, and the other to supply fresh air. If you have the extra space and energy to build them, light traps are fine; but they are more important for safe access to the darkroom than

for the movement of fresh air. An air-conditioning unit of about one-quarter ton would seem to be an ideal solution for a humid darkroom. But you can't operate an air-conditioner, high-wattage enlarger bulb, an electronic timer and several safelights all off the same power line and still expect any consistency in time or light value from your enlarger. If you have a separate 110V line (220V for a three-quarter ton model), then fine. If you are working toward an odorless darkroom, an ultra-refinement would be the use of Defender's 18-F which has eliminated the hypo smell from fixer and replaced it with a faint lavender!

Equipment

Upstairs or downstairs, very large or uncomfortably small, your darkroom should be built around a good enlarger. Unfortunately, there are not as many fine enlargers to choose from as there are fine cameras. One of the finest lines of enlargers you'll find anywhere in the world is the Omega. It's the recommendation of this writer that you try to get an Omega enlarger, even if only a second-hand model. It may mean spending a few extra dollars, but an enlarger of this caliber is something you can use for many, many years of photographic pleasure. Unlike the family car, you won't be trading it on a new model each year. (Refer to the chapter *Which Enlarger? Which Paper?*)

The writer says this mostly in tribute to his Omega D-2 enlarger, which has served well for ten years and shows no signs of not being able to go another ten. Newspaper labs, commercial and magazine photographers, and discriminating amateurs everywhere seem to gravitate to this one common bond in photography. [*As is evident throughout this book, author-photographer Nathan is far gone on the Omega. However, there are other fine enlargers available, and some that may fit your purse or purposes better, so make an independent check of the market.—Editor*]

Now we shall run in methods of counting exposure time. Western photographers and Southern photographers, who speak more slowly, if not more clearly, will take 7 seconds to say "one-thousand-and-one" through "one-thousand-and-five," while the same "standard" count in the Eastern photographer's darkroom will take but 4 seconds. All will vary within the individual darkroom according to how tired the printer is, how many times he's said this fool routine, and how high he has to count by one-thousand-and-seconds. The answer is an electric timer, such as the Time-O-Lite, which counts the preset number of seconds, turning the enlarger on and off at the push of a finger button or the stomp of a foot switch. Not only will you have consistent print timing, but you'll have an accurate way of reducing or increasing the enlarging exposure. The Time-O-Lite in this author's darkroom counts the seconds from 1 to 60, and the markings are large enough to permit intermediate settings in half-seconds.

In choosing a tank, the Nikor stainless is your best bet. It is easy to load, easy to clean, dries quickly, and will not warp. Nikor tanks come in one- to eight-reel sizes; agitation in the one- and two-reel sizes may be conveniently accomplished by rotating the tank. In the larger sizes, a rod that lifts the reels is furnished for agitating. The same tank may be used for both 120 film size and 35mm, by adding 35mm reels to your purchases. Always wash tanks thoroughly when emptied and rinse again as a precaution before using. The plastic FR tank has a spindle which rotates the film during development. If heat is used to speed tank drying for reuse, care must be taken to avoid warping. Fanned heat is the best procedure—or a clean, dry towel.

Glass graduates are the easiest type to clean, and you don't run into the problem of chipping, but they have the disadvantage of being without handles, and come no larger than in quart sizes. For mixing solutions, a gallon-size enamel graduate is the handiest. Nail polish may be used to cover up small chips, and will not harm developer or hypo solutions. Plastic funnels (some come equipped with filters) are inexpensive, and a variety of sizes is useful.

Metal film hangers are needed for developing cut film in tanks, and may also be used for hanging film. Remember, you'll need enough clips to weight the bottom of the roll to minimize curling while drying.

Plastic, enamel, stainless steel, and hard-rubber trays are available, and which you use is a matter of personal preference. There are also sets, in three colors (red, white and black) to assist in identifying solutions. A 5x7 glass tray is useful for reducing and intensifying, and a white enamel tray for toning.

If your enlarging bulb burns out, you'll be stuck, as no ordinary house light bulb can replace it, so have a couple of spares. Even though the bulb has long life, a blown fuse would be the end of it.

Your pocketbook and particular needs will guide you in selecting the easel. Be sure the masking arms move easily and are true, and that the grooves are easy to find for inserting paper.

A paper trimmer is a good investment; you'll find as you go along how much you need it. For trimming mounted prints, the matte knife and straightedge will save wear and tear on your trimmer. It's hard to repair the damage once the blade is out of alignment.

If you start out without an electric dryer, a blotter book or chrome ferrotype tins will save time and space. Ferrotype tins are discussed at length in the Print Finishing chapter. See chart on pages 10 and 11 for other darkroom needs.

The term "safelight" is a relative rather than an absolute term; remember that there is a proper use and purpose for this darkroom item, just as for every other item used in the photographic process. Orthochro-

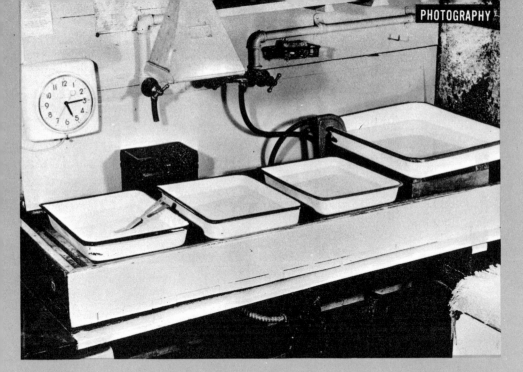

Use fresh chemicals when you start, and discard them when you're through. It is in the darkroom that you convert your great ideas into fine pictures! Too much space in the darkroom can become almost as great a problem as not enough. Arrange your enlarger to be within a step or two of the developing tray. Maintain a dry side and a wet side in the darkroom, and proceed accordingly.

Safelights with interchangeable filters are the best investment. Filter disk is selected according to type of material (contact paper, enlarging paper, Varigam, ortho film, pan film, etc.) that you are handling. Remember, no radio on when you're handling film: the dial throws light.

matic film may be developed in red safelight, and inspected all along the line. Panchromatic film (including Verichrome Pan) may be inspected for a few seconds at a time at a distance of four feet by green safelight (Series 3 Kodak filter), after the halfway developing time has been reached. The best method is to check the safety of your safelight by leaving paper partially covered at a given working distance from the light for five or ten minutes, then developing. If there is any difference in tone between the covered and uncovered half, you'll know the distance of your working light isn't safe.

For general darkroom illumination, extra safelights may be placed in an overhead lighting fixture, or at any distance of 8 to 10 feet from your working area. Be sure this is switched off when processing film, and that the light switch for the white light is not confused with it—which could cause an unfortunate accident.

The following chart indicates the more commonly used filters available for Kodak safelights. ●

FILTER	COLOR	FOR USE WITH
Series OA	Greenish yellow	Contact and enlarging papers
Series 2	Dark red	Orthochromatic films, plates
Series 3	Dark green	Panchromatic films, plates
Series 7	Green	Infrared materials

Automatic Varigam Control*

Darkroom
Needs

Signaling Timer (minutes)

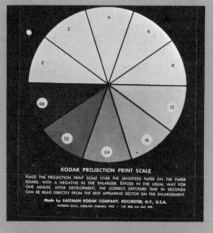

Projection Print Scale

Paper Trimmer

Enlarger Easel

Paper Safe

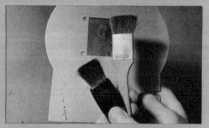

Camel's-Hair Brushes

In addition to items shown below, these complete your darkroom:

Tanks and reels, hangers, clips
Graduates; stirring rods; funnel
Thermometer
Washing hose, filter
Sponge, chamois or film
    squeegee
Film clips; glassine envelopes
Brown jugs (gallon, ½-gallon)
Developer replenisher
Hypo, acid hardener
Negative reducers, intensifier
Rubber apron, gloves
Anti-foggant; hypo test solution

Enlarger and cover
Enlarging lens and lens cap
Extra enlarger bulbs
Projection and contact paper
Filter set (for Varigam)
Three trays (8x10 or larger)
Short stop concentrate
Wash-tray siphon
Plate glass (8x10 or 11x14)
Print roller or squeegee
Ferrotype tins and or dryer*
Blotter book or blotter roll
Tacking iron*

Dry-mounting tissue
Print mounts
Matte knife, straightedge
India ink, pens
Spotting colors, sable brush
Toner
Masking tape; labels; scissors
Cotton; paper toweling;
    Airwick
Glass push pins; carbor tet
Chemical scales*, glass beakers
Enlarger foot switch*
Enlarger timer (seconds)

Contact Printer* or Frame

Enlarger Focusing Aid

Safelight

Film & Paper Developer

Dry-mounting Press*

Anti-Static Spray

*Luxury Items—get them if you can

Right, photos show only some of the developers and
replenishers available (paper developer Dektol is
included since it can be diluted for negative use).

Developing Negatives

by

Simon Nathan

PHOTOGRAPHICALLY speaking, there are no truer words than these: *You can develop your negatives only once!* A good negative doesn't mean that a good print automatically will result, but it is the first item you need to start working toward a good print. And a good negative is the result of correct exposure and correct development.

An exposure meter is a very handy item to have, particularly indoors where there is no other way to measure the amount and intensity of incandescent or fluorescent lighting, daylight filtering in, etc. But outdoors in daylight a meter isn't essential for getting correctly exposed negatives. That small but extremely valuable piece of paper that comes with the roll of film suggests f. openings for various conditions of sun and shade, such as bright sun, hazy sun, cloudy bright, and cloudy dull or open shade. Use this simple, for-free chart as the basis for exposure on your next dozen rolls; if you can't determine the difference between "bright sun" and "hazy sun" you are deluding yourself to think that you can master the use of a photo-electric exposure meter. And use the recommended developing times suggested by the manufacturer of your developer. You'll be on your way to consistently better negatives.

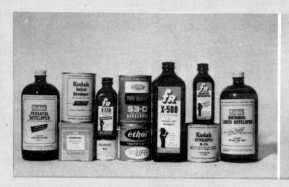

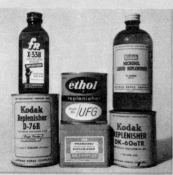

 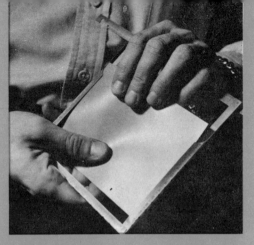

You'll never see this much light around unless you're loading film for practice, but the idea is that the proper way to load a film-developing hanger is shown at left. Photo above right is next-worst way to handle film; possibly the worst way is to keep film in direct contact with sandpaper and rusty nails.

Time-&-Temperature vs. Inspection

Before we put our film into the developer we'll look at a few preliminary considerations. There are two basic methods of developing film—in whatever developer you prefer. These are 1) by time and temperature and 2) by inspection. We mention *time-and-temperature* first, since that is the procedure used by most photographers. Note that we don't say that this is the best method, but perhaps it is the easiest. Simply, it means that at a given temperature (68 degrees is usually best) the film is developed for a specified time that is related to the temperature. As the temperature increases, the length of developing time will decrease proportionally.

Development *by inspection* is more useful in the handling of sheet film, for the photographer who wishes to expend this slight effort. There comes a time in every photographer's diary—and frequently, too—when he wishes that he had developed a certain negative differently. Inspection of the individual films while developing is one of the best methods of controlling the contrast. You can exercise this control either by "pulling," or removing, the negative before the normal developing time has been reached, or by continuing the development beyond the projected total developing time, depending on your subject matter and possible exposure errors.

It should be noted that the 5½-foot length of a 36-exposure roll of 35mm film does not lend itself readily to inspection development, at least not more of it than a few frames at the end of the roll on the outer part of the developing reel. However, if the whole roll is known to contain the same type subject matter, taken under the same or similar (adverse, usually) lighting conditions, there is a definite advantage to examining the developing progress under a safelight (Wratten Series 3, green for panchromatic film) halfway through the total developing time and, again, just before the film is due to be removed from the developer for transfer to short stop and hypo. At this point you may find that additional developing time will be necessary. The benefit of this extra step may show itself in hours saved in printing "difficult" negatives.

It's no easy matter to judge a partially developed negative in the weak light of a green safelight. For one thing, it is difficult to see in such low light; also, negatives generally appear to be more dense than they actually are. This is because you are seeing the image by reflected light, and before the unused silver halide has been removed from the emulsion by the hypo. At first you may be tempted to remove the negative from the developer a bit sooner than the projected developing time. Here's a suggestion to aid you in better judging your negatives under the safelight: Shoot a pair of negatives (sheet film would be easier, but you can adapt the idea to roll film) at the same exposure. Develop one negative for the normal time, run it through the short stop and then wash it. Look at it in white light, so you'll learn the characteristics of a normal, unfixed negative. Held to the viewing light, this unfixed negative reveals its true density. By *reflected* white light you are able to see that one side (the emulsion side) is nearly black in highlight areas and milky-colored in the shadows, but still shows some detail. The reverse, or back side, doesn't show any of the image, except the brighter highlights if the scene is one of high contrast. Now begin developing the

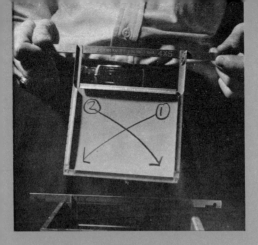

When developing sheet film in hangers, best method of agitation is to lift hanger all the way out of developer, then drain hanger diagonally—first time, one corner down, and next time the alternate corner down. This agitation method is superior to jiggling the hanger against side of the developing tank.

second negative, and use the first negative for a comparative examination of the second one, both under the safelight, as development progresses. By the time you've fixed the second negative, you'll have a pretty good idea of how to develop by inspection.

Tanks and Agitation

Scratch an old-time photographer on the subject of developing methods and he'll surely tell you that there's nothing like the days gone by, when he personally developed as many as thirty sheets of 8x10 film in one quart of developer in a very small 8x10 tray. Historically speaking, the tray method goes back to the time of the itinerant photographer whose darkroom was a tent and whose equipment traveled on horseback. There just weren't any film hangers or stainless-steel Nikor reels. True, tray developing meant scratches and finger marks—but these didn't detract from the relative newness, the uniqueness of a photograph. As the photographer's province expanded and the photograph became commonly accepted as more than a feat of magic, the standards rose. Developing tanks and film holders of numerous types followed as a logical aid to simplify and increase photographic output.

Today, many photographers have never used trays and know only of the reels for rolls and hangers for sheet film—and many of them do not know the procedure and importance of proper agitation of the film during development. No two photographers will agitate film in the exact same manner, but the one who conforms to the principles of good agitation will produce the better-printing negatives. Improper agitation will cause a loss of film speed (the photographer may think his flash

Draining film hanger in this straight up-and-down position is of little agitation value (although it's better than just shaking racks in developer).

synchronizer or his shutter is slightly off), or excessive contrast—generally, a failure to get the inherent benefits of the film. Consistent and sufficient agitation is directly related to time-and-temperature in film developing. The lack of, or a minimum of, agitation causes the development to be slowed down and be uneven.

More obvious damage due to improper agitation will show in a picture taken of a light object against a darkened (filtered) sky. The light object (dark on the negative, of course) appears as a streak into the thinner parts of the negative, as related to their position in the developer. A reverse of this effect will appear as streaks in the high-density (more heavily exposed) areas, and this is caused by unused de-

Roll film is loaded here onto a Nikor reel. First film is separated from paper backing to which it is attached with tape. You do this in dark by feel.

Depress spring clip in center of Nikor reel and slip end of film under. Hold reel so that you'll be winding in same direction as the reel spirals.

Film winds itself right onto reel. Fingers holding film act as guide for edges. Other hand turns Nikor reel steadily to take up film as it's fed.

Deep Nikor tank can take more than two rolls; rod is used to stack and lower reels into tank. Cover is removed (with lights out) to agitate (raise rod).

veloper (usually high energy type) "sliding" down from an unexposed area where it has no developing task to perform, and streaking into an exposed, or high-density section.

Another effect of faulty agitation with sheet film is "surge marks" and these are caused by developer surging through the holes at the edge of the film hanger. This fault results from a modest attempt at agitation known as "jiggling the film ever so slightly," but not lifting it from the developer: it is generally done by the photographer who knows he's supposed to agitate his film because other photographers do, and the sound of the hangers clinking against the tank satisfies his mind as to this requirement. Needless to say, he doesn't know why he should lift the film from the developer and, for about five seconds, allow the old developer to drain back into the tank.

Nikor 35mm reels wind film on from center; major difference is way film attaches to center of reel. Learn to "curve" film by hand, not with film guide.

Tear off leader on 36-exposure 35mm rolls, either before or after winding film onto reel, and you'll have a better fit. Leader has no developable image.

Occasional brushing for Nikor reels removes the collection of scum that accumulates from continued use. Hot water and soap won't hurt reel one bit.

Each time you drain the hangers you hold one corner down, alternating the two bottom corners. It is especially important that you do this at least twice at the start of the developing so that your films will be covered evenly with developer, and any air bubbles which may have formed on the way down the first time will be broken up. If this isn't done, air bubbles will appear as fuzzy circles in the denser areas of the developed negative. Repeat this draining procedure once each minute, alternating the draining corner of the hanger each time. Don't feel that you'll be helping yourself to an even better negative through *constant* agitation: the result of this will be excessive contrast. Standardize your method of agitation and you'll soon reap the benefits in better prints.

Roll-film users who develop more than two rolls at a time (in a Nikor tank) should put their reels on a stainless-steel rod, by means of which all the reels can be agitated at once. If you develop a single roll in a plastic tank, agitation is accomplished by turning the projecting handle, alternating clockwise and counterclockwise directions; agitate constantly for the first 15 seconds, then once every minute for a period of approximately 5 seconds. The main thing is, whatever interval of agitation you use, do it consistently for consistent results. Single- or multiple-roll stainless-steel tanks do not have a projecting handle for turning the reel: you simply lift the tank and agitate the solution by revolving it slowly and turning the tank upside down.

Agitation in the hypo is also important and will assure you of even and more rapid fixing. The washing process, too, will be aided by occasional agitation to break up air bubbles in the water.

"Fine Grain"

In the very early days of photography, prints were the same size as the glass plates on which the pictures were taken.

Left, plastic developing tank has advantage of lower initial cost and adjustability to variety of film sizes. Below, film-pack and sheet film tank is Nikor, of stainless steel; this type eliminates bulkiness of individual hangers and requires less developer working solution. Loaded, it is light-tight.

Roll-film system by Nikor is lifetime investment, and expandable. At left is a single 35mm unit to which additional reels and the deep developing shell can be added, as shown at right: that stack of reels can hold 280 double-frame 35mm exposures for a single developing venture. Beyond that, there's a deeper tank that can hold eight size-120 reels. Drying time between uses is almost nil; just hot-water rinse, wipe.

As enlargers were introduced for projection printing, and camera and film sizes became smaller, photographers began to be aware of graininess in their prints. (In a negative, the image you see is made up of countless tiny, developed particles of silver; when these particles, or grains, clump together so that they become noticeable in the print, we say that the print —and negative—is grainy.) Also, as film speeds were increased there was a disproportionate increase in the grain of the film (that is, the film was manufactured with an inherent tendency to produce grainy negatives). Requirements of the motion-picture industry were responsible for bringing about new fine-grain films as well as fine-grain developers.

The words "fine grain" as we understand them today refer primarily to film that is manufactured with a finer grain structure, with the accompanying necessity of longer exposure. As related to A.S.A. (American Standards Association) ratings, the "faster" a film is rated, the coarser its grain will be. This is another way of expressing the fact that the more light-sensitive a film is, the more silver grains will be present in its emulsion. Here's where we bring into consideration the phrase "fine-grain developer"— which actually is a misnomer, since this type of developer can only minimize the clumping action of the silver grains in the emulsion.

In 1926 the Eastman Kodak Company brought out their still-famous D-76 fine-grain developer. In 1945, Kodak came out with Microdol. Now, if you travel far enough and talk to enough photographers you'll find exponents of both of these developers, and if you have time here are some of the things you'll hear:

D-76: This developer will give you maximum emulsion speed in combination with minimum grain, by overall comparison with other developers. It provides maximum shadow detail in long-scaled negatives. When used for prolonged development, it produces a minimum of fog.

The average developing time at 68 degrees for normal negatives from Eastman Verichrome Pan roll film is 12 minutes. Quart quantities of D-76 cost about 25% less than Microdol; and if that isn't a great enough saving, its formula is available on request from Eastman Kodak. D-76 working time can be cut by one half through the substitution of Kodalk for the borax content in equal amounts. Without replenishment, one gallon will develop twenty size-120 rolls, but with a necessary increase in developing time based on the total volume of the working solution. Life of the developer can be extended five to ten times by use of a replenisher (D-76R, available in gallons only); replenishment has the important advantage of permitting consistent developing times (that is, with no increase in developing time for each roll). D-76 is regarded as moderate fine-grain and clean-working (free from sludge and scum).

Microdol: Eastman brought this onto the market in 1945 to replace DK-20 and to eliminate its main handicap, the sludge condition. It is available in every conceivable package size from pints to 48 gallons in just-add-water powders, and in quarts in liquid form.

Facts: There is some loss in emulsion speed, it has a replenisher, developing times are slightly longer than both DK-20 and D-76, and unfortunately there is no formula available. To many, this last makes the developer too expensive to utilize, but to others the availability of Microdol in liquid quarts may be just the answer. It has good keeping qualities and a simple modification for ultra-fine-grain processing. Briefly, this modification is: expose film one full stop additional (larger), add two tablets of Kodak Anti-Fog No. 1 per quart of Microdol, increase developing time 10% and agitate almost constantly throughout the developing time.

Before you settle on any developer, it would be wise to consult the simple chart for the film-and-developer combination best suited for good results. If you expect to intermix all types of photographic subjects under different types of lighting conditions, you'll have to be prepared to accept and to print from compromised negatives—certainly no reward for fine equipment and a good pictorial eye.

From time to time photographers hear about some new and sensational developer which either produces grain so fine that it can't be measured or gives an increase in emulsion speed so great that modern meters can't handle the calibrations. Next time you hear these claims, warn yourself that (1) grain size is controlled by the manufacturer of the film, as is (2) the speed or sensitivity of the film. American manufacturers tend to rate their films conservatively as to true speed, so that the emulsion-speed loss doesn't show up as greatly with many soft-working fine-grain developers. For the same reason, in the case of a full-speed fine-grain developer like D-76 you're going to think your meter or shutter is off, if you shoot at the rated speed. Using a full-speed fine-grain developer, the fully developed results can be better if a decreased exposure is given (that is, if the film is rated at a higher working ASA rating than given by the manufacturer). Some call this "increasing the film speed"—but what you are actually doing is fully utilizing a high-energy developer to obtain the maximum benefits of a specific emulsion. Film speed is built into the emulsion by Eastman in Rochester or Ansco in Binghamton. It's the developer you select that determines the value received in terms of "speed."

There are many, many good developers in the fine-grain type, and we have used Kodak D-76 and Microdol not to plug the product of one maker, but as the basis of a comparison. Other really fine developers include Harvey's 777, Edwal's Super 20, Kerofine 800, the Sease formulae, Mallinckrodt's Ultratone, FR's X-33B, Ergol, Capitol, Ethanol, and Promicrol. Possibly you are using one of these because: you liked the shape of the bottle; it was recommended by a camera-store clerk who possibly never developed a roll of film in his life; you read some place that professionals use it; or because it would enable you to take pictures "never before possible." Whatever the developer of your choice, learn to know its limitations, its keeping qualities, and if you are ever in doubt, throw it out. Beneath the label, have a chart for keeping track of how many rolls have been developed, and on the label write the date when it was mixed. When you switch to a new developer, develop a roll of similarly exposed shots in the old developer for purposes of comparison.

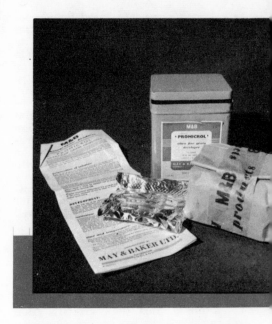

When the cycle of 35mm natural-light photography came along, I learned that $f.1.4$ on my Nikon was being wasted through developers (DK-20, Microdol) that lost a good part of the emulsion speed. For a couple of years we had heard fantastic claims for an English developer by the name of Promicrol. Mostly, it was said to be fine-grain fast-working (i.e., had a relatively short developing time for a fine-grain developer), and was capable of giving emulsion-speed increases beyond the realm of belief. Six months, nearly three hundred rolls, and about $50 ($10 a gallon of working

DEVELOPER AND FILM TEAMS

	Tri-X	Plus-X Verichrome Pan	Pana-tomic-X	KB-14	KB-17	KB-21	Ilford HPS	Ilford FP3	Ansco Supreme
D-76	T	D & T	D	D	D & T	D & T	T	D & T	D & T
Promicrol	T*	D & T	D	D	D & T	D & T	T	D & T	D & T
Microdol	D	D & T		D	T	D & T	D	T	
Kerofine 800	D & T*	D & T	D	D	D & T	D & T	D & T	D & T	D & T
X-500	T*						T	T	
Microphen	D & T	D & T	D	D	D & T	D & T	D & T	D & T	D & T
Ethol UFG	T	D & T	D	D	D & T	D & T	T	D & T	D & T
X-33B	D & T	D & T	D	D	D & T	D & T	D & T	D & T	D & T
X-22		D & T	D	D	D & T	D		D & T	D & T

Above, D is daylight, T is tungsten.
*Recommended for extended emulsion ratings.

Promicrol is expensive, but this is offset by fact that it is such a versatile, flexible fine-grain developer. See text for specific details about Promicrol (shown here in stages of being mixed for use).

solution and a gallon of replenisher) later, I decided that Promicrol is *the* developer for my normal-exposure 35mm and 120-size rolls, as well as a superb developer for "pushing" the developing time to utilize maximum potential of the emulsion.

Promicrol's instruction sheet informs us that "the effective emulsion speed given by Promicrol is either substantially equal to the accepted maximum, or in excess of it. The increase in speed found in practice depends upon the method used to estimate it." Detailed claims are left to photographers using this developer, and by comparison to an emulsion-speed-losing fine-grain developer, Promicrol works out exceedingly well. You may find at first that you have a tendency not to trust the following chart of suggested developing times, and it may take you several "heavy" rolls to become trustful.

PROMICROL DEVELOPING TIMES

FILM	TIME (at 68°)	
	roll film	35mm
Tri-X *	12	13
Verichrome Pan, Plus-X	10½	10
Panatomic-X	8½	8

* Tri-X rating of A.S.A. 200 and 160 is too conservative; use minimum ratings (for 35mm especially) of 250 daylight, 200 tungsten. But try not to shoot Tri-X in sunlight if you use the Tri-X—Promicrol combination, since the resultant negatives will not be "normal."

In terms of grades of paper, the 12-minute roll-film Tri-X negatives were just about always right for printing on normal paper, and the grades needed for the longer developing times were governed pretty much by the subject matter, but were never extremely soft. Tendency was to grades of paper higher in contrast than normal.

At the offset, Promicrol will appear to be clear in color, almost like unused DK-20, and will gradually take on the dark brown color of most "physical" developers. Do not be bothered by this, but merely keep count of the recommended 70-odd rolls per gallon with replenisher. Periodic filtering of the developer after use is recommended for best results. It is also available in quart sizes for the photographer who doesn't develop more than two rolls at a time and who is mainly curious as to its possibilities before going all-out for the larger, more economical quantities. Once in use, the keeping qualities are not much beyond ten weeks, so buy the size that is most economical to you in terms of the number of rolls you put through.

The selection of a fine-grain film and/or a fine-grain developer is not in itself a guarantee of fine-grain results. Here is a list of suggestions applicable to whatever fine-grain process you prefer:

When shooting:

1. Always select the finest-grain film possible for the lighting conditions under

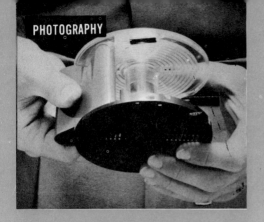

DARK: Lights out, and film is loaded onto plastic reel from outside, working inward by sliding film along the grooves. Tank shown is made by Ansco; other plastic tanks may load from center.

DARK: Lights still out, reel loaded, cover and stirring rod handy nearby, you put the reel into the dry tank. Be careful not to scratch film in any of the processes of handling up to this point.

LIGHTS: Developer has been tested for correct 68-degree working temperature, and is poured into the tank; clock is set and consistent agitation begins. Some workers put developer in before film.

LIGHTS: Consistency of agitation is more important than number of twists per second per minute. Generally, two or three revolutions of reel in tank every minute are adequate. Do it regularly.

which you intend to make your exposures.

2. Don't use outdated film and expect the fine-grain results of fresh film. And film is not "fresh" if you have but three weeks to go until printed expiration date. This expiration date is based on the product's ability to record an acceptable image, and not a whole lot more.

3. Store your film in a cool, dry place before exposure and do not subject it to extreme heat before or after exposure.

4. Fill your negative with the subject matter whenever possible, since enlarging the image also enlarges the grain.

5. Keep exposures on the short side because graininess is more evident in dense

(heavy) negatives than it is in thin ones.

6. Focus carefully: nothing emphasizes grain more than soft focus.

7. Try, whenever possible, to shoot subjects of dissimilar contrast on separate rolls, and alter your developing times accordingly.

When processing:

8. Always try to develop your film as soon after exposure as humanly possible.

9. Select your fine-grain developer according to the emulsion of the film that you exposed and the type of illumination (from very soft to contrasty).

10. Pay close attention to the manufac-

Developer's been poured out, film has had quick rinse, and the fixing-hardening process is complete. Now wash in running water whose temperature is as close to that of developer as possible.

When film's well washed, soft viscose sponge is used to remove excess moisture before hanging up to dry. Last step before sponging can be quick dip in a wetting agent to prevent water streaks.

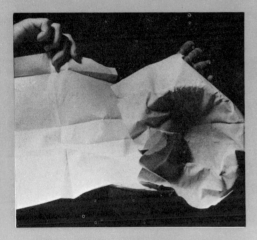

Pour developer through good-quality Scott toweling after use, before pouring it in stock bottle. Impurities you filter out will be plainly visible. These impurities could adhere to your negatives.

Bottle caps are relatively inexpensive and may seem a minor item. But, oh, the trouble they can cause through contamination of expensive developers. Remember to change caps from time to time.

turer's recommendations for developing time and temperature. Most developers give best results when used at 68 degrees. However, Harvey 777 will give very good fine-grain results when used as low as 60 degrees and all the way to 80 degrees; it could be your answer if you are developing your rolls on a trip away from your home lab and can't arrange the ultimate in temperature control. Also, the British developer Capitol is stated to work its best at 77 degrees.

11. Standardize your method for agitation during developing.

12. There should not be more than 10 degrees temperature difference between developer, short stop and hypo for consistent results.

13. Wash water should not run below 60 or above 78 degrees. Colder water takes longer to remove hypo and does not do a thorough job, while warmer water brings you closer to the problem of reticulation; slight reticulation is often confused with grain.

14. Prolonged washing—even at the correct temperature—softens the emulsion and makes it prone to scratches in the drying process. In addition, consider the water as an "abrasive" against the emulsion.

15. Don't employ forced-hot-air drying methods.

Pictorial memories of a happy time in Florida suffer from the negative blemishes shown on contact sheet above. Loaded reel was dropped, denting film inward so that emulsion and backing were in contact at various spots, throughout developing time. Sad result: no image.

Developing Strobe Negatives

So much has been written on the development of strobe negatives that it'd be better to explain away some of the notions you may have heard, and tell you how to decide for yourself. Like automobiles, the repeating flashtubes on the market are becoming more and more powerful. The early 100-watt-second units gave about half the light that the modern battery portable now carries in one third the weight. The earliest models fired their flashtubes at 1/5,000 second with a light so soft that the photographer was required to develop his negative as much as 50% over what would be normal development for flashbulb exposures.

In an effort to create lighter-weight units the light output was curtailed and the gap to the higher "guide number" (see below) was taken up with the recommendation of increased development. So photographers came to expect contrast in their negatives, both from experience with sunlight and their encounters with contrasty flashbulb lighting and photofloods. Another aspect that figured, once portable strobes became commonplace, was their use with roll film and miniature cameras. The small-camera users had learned to expose film at less than the manufacturer's ratings, with the speed losses chargeable to emulsion-speed-losing fine-grain developers. Strobe values were based on these same film speeds, but without the handicap of fine grain as required by the smaller-sized negatives.

It is best, when starting with a strobe light, first to make tests with your normal development and determine your own guide number (an arbitrary number which, when divided by the distance of the light to the subject, indicates the correct *f.* stop for exposure. To do this make a series of exposures at a distance of 10 feet from the subject in an average-sized room with light-colored walls. Start with the smallest opening on your camera—*f.*22, *f.*32, or whatever it may be—and make one

ACUFINE FILM DEVELOPING TABLE

MS	65	68	70	75	80	85	E.I.
anatomic-X	2:30	2:15	2:00	1:40	1:15	1:00	100
n-F	"	"	"	"	"	"	64
-14	"	"	"	"	"	"	64
pan FF	"	"	"	"	"	"	64
-17	3:10	2:40	2:30	2:00	1:40	1:15	160
-21	3:45	3:20	3:00	2:20	1:45	1:30	250
pan F	"	"	"	"	"	"	125
3	4:20	3:45	3:30	2:40	2:20	1:45	250
pan SS	"	"	"	"	"	"	200
lus-X	5:00	4:30	4:00	3:45	2:30	2:00	320
P3	5:20	4:40	4:15	3:20	2:40	2:10	500
pan U	5:45	5:00	4:30	3:30	2:45	2:15	500
ri-X	6:00	5:15	4:45	3:45	3:00	2:20	1200
pan Record	8:45	7:45	7:00	5:30	4:30	3:30	1000
S	"	"	"	"	"	"	1000
per Hypan	"	"	"	"	"	"	1000
MS	**65**	**68**	**70**	**75**	**80**	**85**	**E.I.**
4	3:10	2:40	2:30	2:00	1:40	1:15	64
pan FF	3:45	3:20	3:00	2:20	1:45	1:30	64
7	"	"	"	"	"	"	160
pan F	4:20	3:45	3:30	2:40	2:20	1:45	125
erichrome Pan	"	"	"	"	"	"	320
21	5:00	4:30	4:00	3:45	2:30	2:00	250
lus-X	"	"	"	"	"	"	320
anatomic-X	5:45	5:00	4:30	3:30	2:45	2:15	100
pan SS	"	"	"	"	"	"	200
pan U	7:00	6:00	5:30	4:20	3:25	2:45	500
ri-X	7:30	6:30	6:00	4:45	3:45	3:00	1200
P3	"	"	"	"	"	"	500
P3	"	"	"	"	"	"	250
pan Record	8:45	7:45	7:00	5:30	4:30	3:30	1000
uper Hypan	10:20	8:45	8:00	6:15	5:00	4:00	1000
PS							1000

All times are given in minutes: seconds.

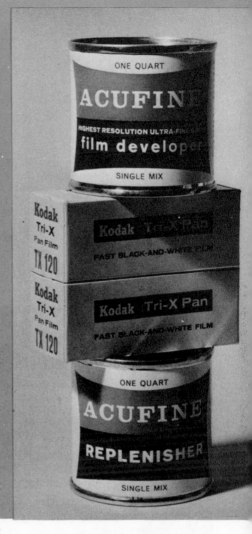

exposure after another of, say, a patient friend sitting on the sofa, each successive shot at a whole f. stop larger opening. If you still have a couple exposures left on the roll, take them with bounce light (off the ceiling, directed slightly toward the subject) starting at f.8 and working toward the larger openings. Develop the roll. Use fresh developer and the manufacturer's recommended developing time for whatever emulsion you are using. Pay close attention to the temperature so that the test will have some validity.

From the group of direct-flash shots (aimed at the subject), the negative which will print on No. 2 ("normal") paper is the one to draw your guide number from. For example, if the f.16 negative will print on normal paper, work backward to reach a guide number by multiplying the f. stop by the distance (10 feet); this gives a guide number of 160. If this number is satisfactory for most of your work, you'll be able to mix strobe, flash and daylight exposures on the same roll or filmpack. In the case of sheet film it will save cluttering up the margins of your holders with hundreds of tiny pencil marks to indicate exposures.

The same factors—softness of light and normal development—which make strobe negatives easier to print should not be sacrificed to create negatives matching those made with harsher sources of light. In other words, don't try to make a strobe negative look like a flashbulb negative. •

Reduction and Intensification

ERRORS of exposure and development fall on both sides of the ideal, easy-printing negative. The first error—incorrect film exposure—is often made by a photographer who feels that he cannot determine exposures without a meter, and after taking the meter reading decides to "add a little for good measure." This results in overexposure and, needless to say, a dense negative—perhaps so dense that it is very difficult to see the separation of tones necessary in a good printing negative. The remedy is to reduce this negative.

As for the second error—incorrect film development—there is also the photographer who adds a couple extra minutes onto his developing time, for good measure . . . not to mention the photographer who doesn't bother to check the temperature of the developer before he begins developing his negatives (and if there is no compensating decrease in his developing time the net result will be a more dense negative at the higher temperature). Here, too, reduction will permit a better print to be taken from the dense-developed negative.

To understand reduction you'd do well, at first, to think of it as a developing-backwards process, because what you are doing is chemically reducing the image, just as in developing you chemically built the image. Presented here are three types of reducers which will cover just about every dense-negative situation, according to the nature of the image. For the darkroom worker who does not have time to weigh out ingredients there are a number of packaged reducers on the market, such as Kodak Farmer's Reducer and Ansco Reducer.

1. Cutting reducer: When a negative is flat or the shadows contain excessive detail or fog, it is desirable to remove a thin layer of silver from the developed image. The change will be much more noticeable in the shadow areas, making for increased contrast over the whole negative. The control is visual, so you'll be able to end the reduction at the point where you have improved the negative to your liking. A warning: practice on unimportant negatives when first using a cutting reducer.

Don't reduce too far. A simple way to slow the action of the reducer is to increase the volume of the water in the working solution. The operation is simple to repeat if you feel that further reduction is required, but there's no going back if you've reduced too far. As in developing, agitation is important during reduction also.

Before using the following formula for cutting reducer, make sure that your negative is well washed, free of hypo. If you are going to reduce some hard-to-print negatives already in your file, soak them for at least ten minutes in clear, running water.

Solution A:
    Potassium ferricyanide........55 *grains*
    Water ....1 *ounce*
Solution B:
    Hypo crystals ....2 *ounces*
    Water ....1 *quart*

Mix the two solutions together (in an enamel tray free of breaks) when you are ready to start, immerse the negative into the tray of reducer and pay close attention to the process of reduction, as it takes place in a matter of minutes, depending on the amount of excess silver built up on your negative. Since the color will be a deep lemon yellow you will be better able to judge the progress by giving the negative a quick rinse in running water to eliminate most of the yellow color, which can mislead you at first as to true negative values. It can be compared to learning to judge prints under a yellow safelight. The excess silver which gave the unwanted extra density in your negative is converted by the ferricyanide to silver ferricyanide. This, in turn, is dissolved by the hypo in the solution. When your negative has been reduced to a more suitable density, place it in running water for 30 minutes and then hang it up to dry.

The *A* solution (potassium ferricyanide and water) can be stored in your darkroom, but once it has been combined with the hypo it will deteriorate rather rapidly. It's safer not to keep potassium ferricyanide around in liquid form because it is a fatal poison.

ense negatives can be improved by reduction; both underexposed and underdeveloped ones can be intensified. Result is a printable neg.

FOR PHOTOGRAPHIC OR
TECHNICAL PURPOSES ONLY

Kodak
CHROMIUM
INTENSIFIER*

POISON

16-OUNCE SIZE
(473 cc.)

EASTMAN KODAK COMPANY

Victor
FINE GRAIN
INTENSIFIER

Potassium ferricyanide was used for reducing the above negative, which shows a friendly seal sunning himself in the Bronx Zoo. As it appears in center (most dense) section, negative could be printed on No. 1 (soft) paper. Right-hand portion of negative shows to what extent negative can be reduced, but is now too thin. Band at left shows proper contrast for a normal (No. 2) printing negative. On the original exposure the seal's cave was the same density clear across the negative, so you can readily judge change from that. In photo at left, negatives treated with potassium ferricyanide have been immersed in hypo and are returned to film hanger for thorough wash in running water.

2. *Proportional reducer:* This method of reduction removes the silver from the negative in proportion to the amounts carried in the different areas of density. That is, it takes a little silver from the shadow areas and a lot from the highlight areas, keeping the negative in scale. It is intended for negatives of excessive contrast, not those of normal contrast (a negative may be very heavy, or dense, and still be of normal contrast).

Solution A:
  Water ....*16 ounces*
  Potassium permanganate......2 grains
  10% solution of sulfuric
    acid ....*¼ fluid ounce*
Solution B:
  Water ....*48 ounces*
  Ammonium persulfate....1½ ounces

Handle the sulfuric acid with special care as it can cause severe burns to your skin. A 10% solution is made by adding 1 part sulfuric to 9 (equal in volume) parts of water. *Be sure you don't add the water to the acid,* because this could cause it to boil and spatter your skin.

Mix one part of A *to three parts of* B *for the solution in which to reduce your negative.* After sufficient reduction, put the film in a weak solution of sodium bisulfite (⅓ ounce of sodium bisulfite to a quart of water) to remove the brownish stain. This is followed by a thorough washing of the negative before drying.

3. *Super-proportional reducer:* If you want to "cut" or reduce your highlights without affecting the shadow areas, then you'll want to use this method. Before you start, note that if you need only one print from this negative your time will be better spent on other darkroom chores. Generally speaking, you'd use a super-proportional reducer to "adjust" a negative to fit a paper that is available in only one grade of contrast (an example is Eastman Kodak's Illustrator's Special), or if you have a negative from which you have to make a considerable number of enlargements, since this correction will reduce the printing time.

Buy a good brand of ammonium persulfate (and in not too large a quantity, since it isn't something you'll be using very often); it is important that the chemical be of uniform strength and purity.

Water ....*32 ounces*
Ammonium persulfate ....*2 ounces*
Sulfuric acid ....*¾ dram*

Use one part of this stock solution with two parts of water.

Remove the negative before the reduction has been completed to the degree you think best, as there will be a slight continuation of the reducing action during the water rinse and before you put the negative into fresh hypo.

One of the three above-mentioned methods for reduction should cover any fog, overexposure, overdevelopment or contrast problem which may come up. However, the technique of *local reduction* has not been discussed up to this point: It takes practice to become proficient at it, and if you've never tried to reduce a negative before, this is hardly the way to begin. An example of a negative that could be improved through local reduction is one where you have a subject half in the shade and half in contrasty sun lighting. You need only to take down the highlights on one side of the negative, without altering the shade area of the scene. Use a mild solution of the cutting reducer (method 1) with a brush or cotton as applicator. Rinse frequently to check the action of the reducer and hold the negative so that the working solution does not streak across areas of the picture which you don't want to change.

Intensification of Negatives

"Thin" negatives—negatives that are somewhat more difficult to print than "heavy" negatives, and cause you to waste more paper, need not be discarded if you are willing to expend a little time and trouble to doctor them up by a process aptly called *intensification.* Thin negatives result from underexposure, from underdevelopment, or a combination of both. Underexposure may be caused by using too slow a film for the lighting conditions and nature of your subject. But take heart, all may not be lost. Here's what you can do.

First, make sure that the negative you wish to salvage is completely free from hypo. To be certain of this, give it an extra-long wash. Otherwise, the chemicals you will apply to it may cause unevenness and indelible spots and streaks. If you have several thin negatives on a roll, don't treat them all at once as they may require different degrees of change.

Intensifiers are of two types: the indirect, in which the image is bleached out and then redeveloped, and the direct, in which intensification is carried out by immersion in a single solution. Increase in contrast and density takes place in two ways. First, by changing the image from black to a warmer color, which filters out the blue rays (to' which most printing papers are highly sen-

sitive) and so increases the effective density. Second, by adding complex metallic salts or a metal to the silver image.

The simplest method is the first, and involves dissolving a powdered preparation called Victor Fine-Grain Intensifier. The solution should be discarded and all receptacles well washed immediately after use. Distilled water is suggested by the manufacturer. Wearing rubber gloves, mix the contents of the vial in a porcelain or glass beaker, and if any sediment forms, pour off the top clear solution into a porcelain or glass tray. Take the wet negative, hold it with a clothes pin, and dip it quickly in the solution. Stand by, as things will happen fast. Five to ten seconds (minimum) to five minutes (maximum) is enough to do the trick. Remove, wash ten minutes in running water and hang to dry. Over one minute in the bath will change the color of the negative, producing a yellow-brown color which is permanent and non-objectionable. If you think you've gone too far, slip the negative into fresh hypo solution, wipe it with cotton, and you have your original back and can start all over again.

For local intensification (in only one area of the negative) pre-soak the negative for ten minutes, then apply Victor solution to the weak parts with a soft brush, or cotton on a stick, until you have the desired density—wash and dry.

A technique you may want to try sometime to get a very snappy, brilliant negative for blowing up to large exhibition or

Print above is quite gray, yet it's the best that can be made from negative on right, using grade 4 paper or No. 10 Varigam filter. The negative was hardly worth filing in this condition, so it was intensified in the Victor single-solution intensifier. After a three-minute soaking it was washed for ten minutes in running water; then negative was sponged, dried. Now see facing page.

mural size: underdevelop your film in fine-grain developer (such as D-76), fix and wash. Then re-develop it for 15 to 60 seconds in Victor Intensifier, and you'll see the contrast build up. Wash thoroughly, dry and print. All operations with Victor Intensifier may be carried on in daylight.

A second and more complicated method of intensifying is by use of Kodak's chromium intensifier, which comes in a 16-ounce size packet. This packet contains two envelopes, one for making the bleach bath, and one for making the clearing bath. Follow the directions inside the package for mixing. Harden the negative first in Kodak Special Hardener SH-1, then bleach thoroughly at 65 to 70 degrees, for 3 to 5 minutes—or until the image is bleached yellow. Rinse in water and immerse in the clearing bath until the yellow color is removed and a nearly white negative image remains. This will take about two minutes at 68 degrees. Rinse in 68-degree water for five minutes, and re-develop in a nonstaining fast-working developer (such as Kodak Versatol or Dektol) until the white image is blackened completely. No fixing is needed. Just wash for 20 minutes and hang to dry. The clearing and re-developing should be carried out in artificial light or weak (diffused) daylight.

With the Kodak intensifier you may repeat the process to add greater intensification, but you can't wipe it out. Try both methods to see which one is most satisfactory, and then stick to it. •

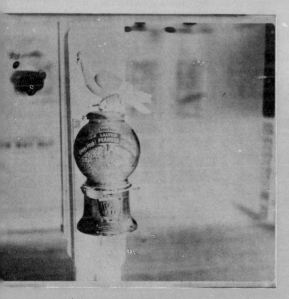

Left is intensified version of negative on opposite page. Print above was made on grade 2 paper (No. 5 Varigam filter could be used), with slight amount of dodging of body of pigeon, and some burning-in of highlights on the side of gum machine. On 4x5 negatives and larger, local intensification will permit balancing of negative so that the burning-in won't be necessary.

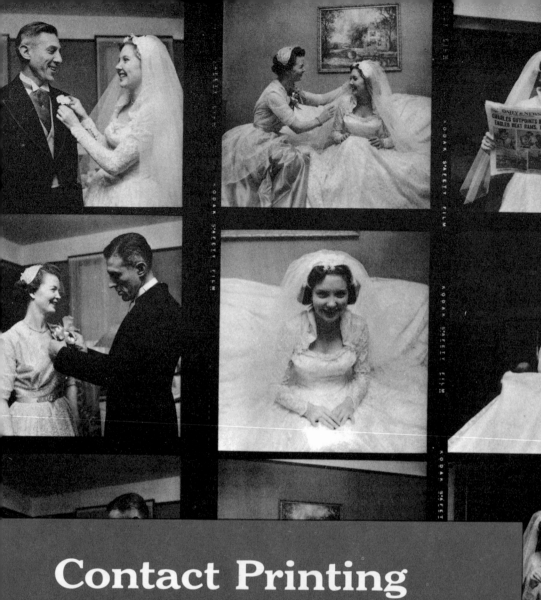

Contact Printing

Never minimize the importance of making good, clear contact prints.

Cut your 120 reflex negs into strips of fours; place them emulsion side up on inside glass surface of frame.

Complete assembly shows sheet of enlarging paper placed with emulsion in contact with emulsion of negs. To make exposure, place under light, which passes through lens of enlarger. Diaphragm controls the exposure.

THE TERM *contact printing* means to print negatives in direct contact with the printing paper rather than by projection. Simply as it is stated, it is becoming a lost art in this day of the miniature camera and the autofocusing enlarger. Chances are, that unless you are an honest-to-goodness professional with a gigantic view camera, your only contact prints in the course of a year are the cards you make at Christmas-time and the occasional proofs you make from your rolls of film. These latter-mentioned "contacts" can hardly be called prints, since almost anything goes, just so there's a decent enough image for you to see whether the subject's eyes are open or if the action has been stopped.

You may say that you don't have space for one of those monster contact-printers in your petite closet darkroom—and, furthermore, they aren't for free. However, with as little equipment as a 10x12-inch piece of good-quality plate glass you can make high-quality contact prints. An 8x10 printing frame with a spring back is at least as good, and the choice will be one of personal preference.

Raise the head of your enlarger just high enough that the area of light passing through the wide-open lens covers the whole of your plate glass or printing frame without any cutoff at the corners. Using just a piece of plate glass, first place a sheet of enlarging paper on the baseboard of the enlarger (the room lights are off now and you are doing this under the same safelights used for enlarging). Face the emulsion side upward toward the lamphouse. Place your strips of roll film directly onto the paper, their emulsion in contact with the emulsion of the enlarging paper. Place the glass on top.

Reflex 120 rolls can be cut into three strips of four frames each (and later cut into pairs for easier filing), or cut into four strips of three, and placed side by side on the sheet of 8x10 enlarging paper.

Size 120 rolls which give 2¼x3¼-inch negatives should be cut into pairs, and the negatives made with the 120 Omega camera (they're 2¼x2¾) can be handled as strips of three, horizontally on the paper. Rolls of 35mm should be cut into strips of five or six according to your own filing system. (The filing of 35mm negatives in rolls is contrary to the whole idea of delicate handling of this type of film and is not recommended.) One full roll of 35mm strips will ordinarily require more than one 8x10 sheet, so divide up the number of strips for easier handling. Four 4x5 negatives fit an 8x10 sheet well enough. Note that all of these prints will be without borders; if you desire bordered prints, choose them from your selections based on the whole roll contact-sheet prints. If you plan to contact filed negatives which have been already cut into pairs or singles, the least frustrating way of handling them is to confact fewer per sheet to avoid the problem of lining up the negatives.

It goes without saying—but we have to say it here—that there are bound to be some uneven exposures in a roll of twelve negatives, unless you've just shot twelve pictures of the same subject at the same exposure and without any fluctuation on the part of old Sol above. This means that one over-all printing exposure will make certain prints either too light and/or too dark. Be not discouraged—all you have to do is to see to it that those negatives which didn't receive enough light in the camera don't get too much light during the overall exposure for the sheet of contacts. If the dense negatives in the group are bothersome, arrange for these to have additional exposure from the light of the enlarger. This might be expressed as dodging or burning-in, for that is essentially what it is, except that whole negatives are involved rather than sections of a single negative as in the enlarging process.

To do this, select a grade of paper of contrast suitable for most of the exposures on the sheet. Cut little squares of cardboard the size of a negative frame; lay one over a thin negative right on top of the plate glass for that part of the exposure you wish to dodge, and then reach in and flick it from its position. Burning-in can be accomplished with a hole the dimensions of a single negative centered in a sheet of lightweight cardboard. Two L-shaped arms

  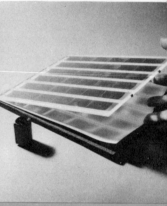

Useful item for contact printing of 35mm rolls is the Multi-Printer, above. It holds neg in correct alignment and sequence. Loaded, you close assembly over sheet of 8x10 enlarging or contact paper. Cardboard rectangles can be neatly used to reduce exposure on thin negatives in roll, or to increase exposure on the ones which are dense.

At left is the handy Leitz' Eldia combination printer for making either film or paper positives.

Contact print frame method of proofing rolls is shown above. Picture indicates that two negs, top left, are thin and are being masked from the light source with a cardboard rectangle. Hand-held dodger in center of photo is performing same task.

Two negatives, above, on this contact sheet are overexposed and need extra printing time. Balance of the sheet is protected from the light source by the L-shaped piece of black cardboard. Cut various shapes of cardboard for such jobs.

of cardboard may prove even more versatile, and you'll eventually notice that you can simplify the dodging or burning-in by placing the strip of negatives needing the most attention in either top or bottom position rather than as the center row. Use the diaphragm of the enlarger to control the light so that you provide long enough exposures to make the above corrections as required.

The use of the printing frame involves about the same procedure as working with a sheet of plate glass. Some workers prefer the frame because it assures better contact, and makes it unnecessary to exert occasional pressure on the plate glass.

The next step fancier is the use of a multi-light contact printer with a felt or balloon-pressure platen. The first advantage you'll notice is the safelight under the printing glass, which makes it easier to

align the rows of negatives before placing down the contact paper (not enlarging paper, which is far too rapid). Second advantage you'll calculate is that contact paper is less expensive, and this is important in a volume operation. On the other hand, when contact printing with the sheet of plate glass or simple printing frame, you can use an enlarger and your regular enlarging paper. The quality you'll get from straight contact (chloride) paper is amazing, yet frustrating when you start seeking the chloride tones in making a bromide enlargement. Third advantage in a ready-made, fancy-fancy electronic contact printer is that you can "underlay" individual or group negatives with pieces of tissue paper before exposure as a means of exposure control. The separator sheets that come in packages of dry mounting tissue are almost priceless for this purpose.

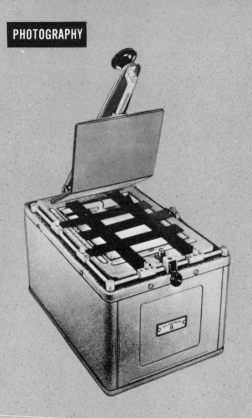

Home model contact printer has adjustable masks for putting borders on many sizes of negatives. Ruby light switches off once the cover is closed.

One very good contact printer, Time-O-Lite's model 80, has two special features which are of great value to the darkroom worker: an intensity control for the illumination that permits control of exposure times for a wide variety of speeds in contact printing papers; second, a movable diffusion control which raises and lowers according to the degree of diffusion desired. As much as 70% light reduction is possible. The built-in timer is useful in making numerous prints at the same exact exposure or to enable measured correction should the initial choice of printing time provide a print which develops either too rapidly or, to the other extreme, hardly develops out at all.

Eastman Kodak, Ansco, Gevaert and others market fine contact papers in a wide choice of surfaces and long range of contrasts. The selection of a particular paper should be the result of a fair trial of the product of each company. Develop a contact print in the same way you handle enlargements. One major difference is that you can use an "O" safelight if you are handling contact papers alone, the advantage being that it is brighter than any other paper safelight. One word of suggestion: learn to make contact prints and enlargements with the same safelight so that you develop and retain given standards for viewing prints in progress. This gets back to the idea of print quality—a topic thoroughly covered in our Enlarging section. For some reasons for making contact sheets, and a sample of one marked up for enlarging reference, see *What's a Good Print?*

The same box of Varigam which can cover most of your enlarging needs is ideally suited for contact printing with the plate glass or printing frame method. For example, you can place the previously mentioned squares of cardboard over the thin negatives, while you expose over-all with a normal (No. 5) filter. Then you lift the shield from the thin negative, mask the other negatives and expose the thin negative through a high number filter. This will give you a better match to the rest of the exposures than an underexposed print from a thin negative on normal paper. •

Time-O-Lite printer has electrical timing, density and illumination control. This printer handles all sizes up to 8x10, has cushion pressure plate.

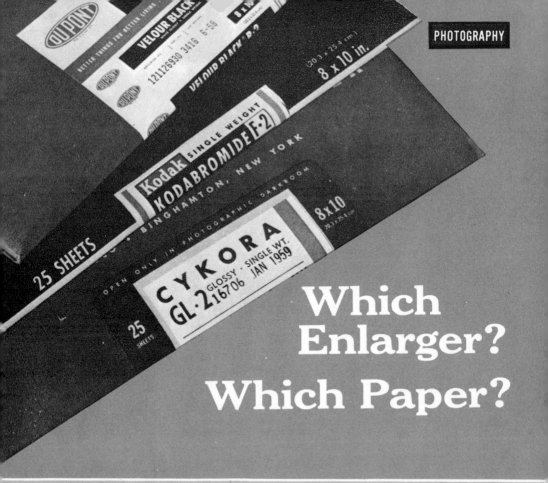

Which Enlarger? Which Paper?

ENLARGING is certainly the most rewarding of all the work you'll do in your darkroom. It is the point where you are combining the resolving power of a fine lens, proper exposure and developing techniques, good composition, and numerous other intangibles, into a finished product: an enlargement!

There are mainly two kinds of enlargements: *good* and *bad*. We'll be dealing with the ingredients for better prints, the first of which—properly exposed and developed negatives—was taken up in the Developing chapter. A "good" negative alone does not assure you of a good picture, as there are many things to learn and to do in the process of turning out a fine enlargement. First you'll need to know just what a good print really is, and then how to attain it. Fortunately, the enlarging process, unlike negative developing, permits the darkroom worker to go back and do it over if the result is not satisfactory. It is what you have to show as a final result that people will judge as being "a good picture."

Any darkroom worker who equips himself with a fine enlarger, such as one of the Omegas mentioned in the Darkroom chapter, will soon realize that while good prints are "developed" in a tray, they are born in the enlarger.

Following is a list of the enlargers available in the Omega line. From these you can select a model which will fit your darkroom requirements (that is, according to the sizes of negatives to be handled, desire for manual or automatic focusing, etc.).

Omega Model	Negative Sizes
A-2 (manual focus)	8mm to 35mm
B-8 (manual focus)	35mm to 2¼x3¼
B-7 (autofocus)	35mm to 2¼x3¼
D-2 (manual focus)	35mm to 4x5
D-3 (autofocus)	35mm to 4x5
E-5 (autofocus)	2¼x2¼ to 5x7

All models listed in the chart can be adapted to "cold light" printing, which some workers prefer for portraits and to minimize the effects of grain, scratches, dust, and retouching marks.

Small-camera negatives which are developed by fine-grain methods yield the best prints when handled with a condenser

Workers dealing in 35mm exclusively will find the Omega A-2 the answer for them; it is also suitable for Minox and other sub-miniature sizes. The colorhead is built in. Omega D-2, center, handles 35mm to 4x5 film sheets via interchangeable lenses and condensers; other accessories are available. Right is Omega's E-5, coldlight for 5x7 to 35mm negs. It's autofocus, and is available with condensers.

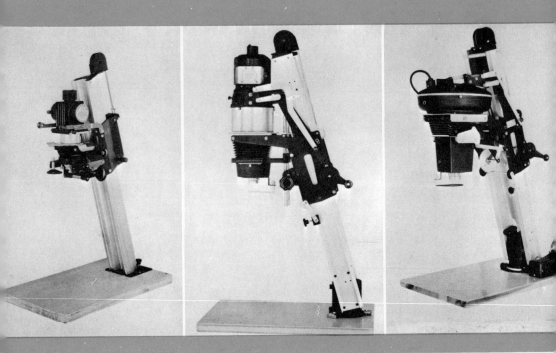

enlarger. This is because there is a condenser (a set of lenses) focusing the entire amount of light from the enlarging bulb through the negative. It directs this light evenly and without hot spots. A condenser enlarger is always faster-printing, from the standpoint of shorter exposures, and it is usually easier to focus because of the wonderfully bright light being sent through the negative.

A discussion of the various enlarger light sources accompanies drawings on a following page.

Whether you choose a manual focusing enlarger, or one that focuses automatically as you change the size of your image on the easel, is pretty much a question of taste governed by a dash of pocketbook. The main thing is that you get started with a *good* enlarger. The lack of automatic focusing need not affect your print quality. An autofocusing enlarger is very time-saving for the darkroom worker who has a lot of variable-size prints to turn out in short length of time. Also it is a boon to the photographer with poor eyesight. As for the inexperienced pho-

tographer the autofocusing enlarger permits him, with a minimum of effort and time, to examine his negative in several variations of size before determining the exact cropping he'll use for his print.

It is likely that you are aware that there are various strengths in the enlarger bulbs available for your Omega or other enlarger. The chances are that you are using the same bulb which was supplied with your enlarger and are fairly satisfied. If you use, say, the 212 bulbs for your general run of enlarging, this will leave the lower wattage 211 bulb for easier handling of thin negatives and the 213 bulb of higher wattage for blasting through the heavier negatives. You should also think of these various strengths of enlarger bulbs as being related to the various speeds of available enlarging paper. If you find a particular paper too "fast" for one bulb (that is, having too short an exposure time to permit any dodging or margin for error), try the next lower bulb for a more suitable scale of exposure times. Bear in mind that a 1-second error on a total exposure time of 10 seconds is only a 10% error, while a 1-second error

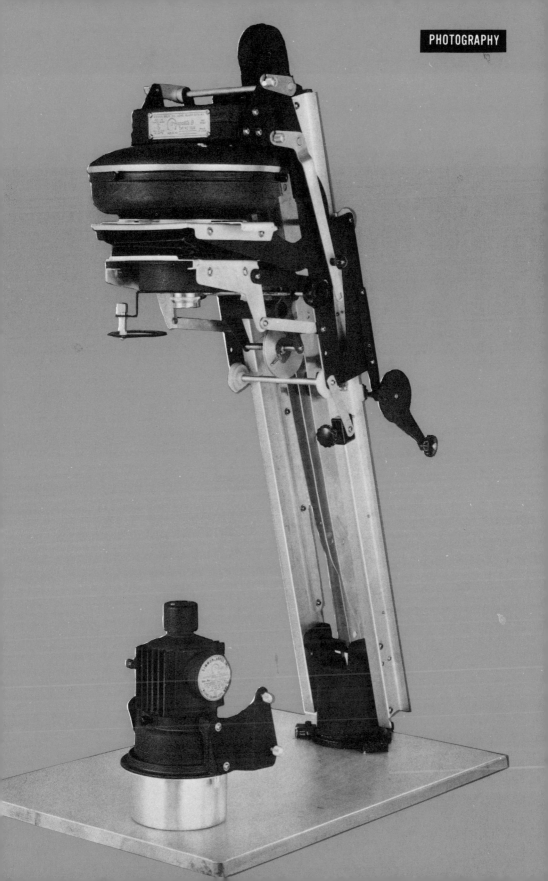

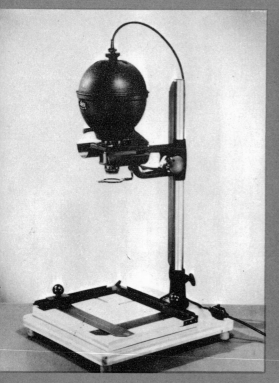

Leitz Focomat enlarger for 35mm is a precision companion for any high-grade 35mm camera and, further, can utilize the f.3.5 Leica taking lens.

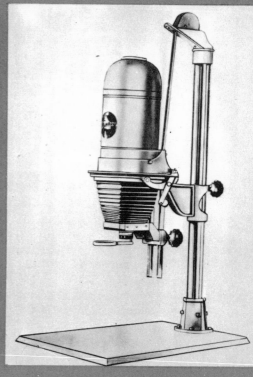

Reasonably priced Sun Ray enlarger Model 45 has a glassless negative carrier, opal diffusion. Baseboard is 18x24; lists slightly over $100, less lens.

on a 2-second exposure is 50% over or under, and won't even yield a print suitable for judging what *would* be a correct exposure.

Enlarging Papers

As noted in the chapter on contact printing, the slowest of the photographic papers are the chloride papers. For enlarging we have bromide papers, which are considerably more light-sensitive, and also chlorobromide papers. Paper comes in a great variety of surfaces, as well as two general weights: single and double. The range is from smooth (with no pattern to interfere with image detail) to rough (with a variety of patterns that minimize detail). In between are fine-grained surfaces which lend themselves to exhibition prints.

Observations that follow are based on Kodabromide (enlarging bromide paper made by Eastman Kodak), Velour Black (enlarging chloro-bromide made by Du Pont), with some special notes and recommendations on Varigam (variable-contrast enlarging paper made by Du Pont). These

are selected merely to provide a basis for comparison. Needless to say, there'll be photographers who are using other brands of enlarging paper, some by the above-mentioned manufacturers and some from other makers of good photographic paper. Whatever type you prefer, if you use it according to the manufacturer's recommendations, and with patience and good sense, you'll reap high rewards in terms of better prints.

As is true of other photo-sensitive materials, enlarging paper will perform at its best when stored away from the dampness in basements and the dry heat of steam radiators. Avoid the odors that you yourself don't like, and your enlarging paper won't have to fight off paint storage fumes, exhaust from the basement gas furnace, etc. One final word: don't expect from outdated paper even a fraction of the high quality attainable from fresh stock!

Kodabromide: This brand of bromide enlarging paper will give rich, brilliant blacks which are ideal for exhibition prints as well as prints intended for reproduction.

Below, top left, the geared up-and-down handle on the Omega D-3 autofocus enlarger permits quick composition and also permits simultaneous focus.

Top center, nylon friction lock keeps the enlarger head in same position for continuous printing.

Top right, manual focusing knob for adjusting the enlarger in situations as needed; one such situation would be where a different printing easel is used. Once this adjustment is made the Omega D-3 becomes an autofocus enlarger as before.

Below, bottom left, a long lamphouse lever arm is used to raise lamphouse for cleaning or for removal of the negative; it works with ease.

Interchangeable condensers are easily installed by raising the lamphouse and releasing two knobs.

Bottom right, lenses for autofocus D-3 are also easily changed and should be stored with lens caps in position. As Omega lenses are easily removed it follows that they are also easily cleaned, one important step to sparkling prints.

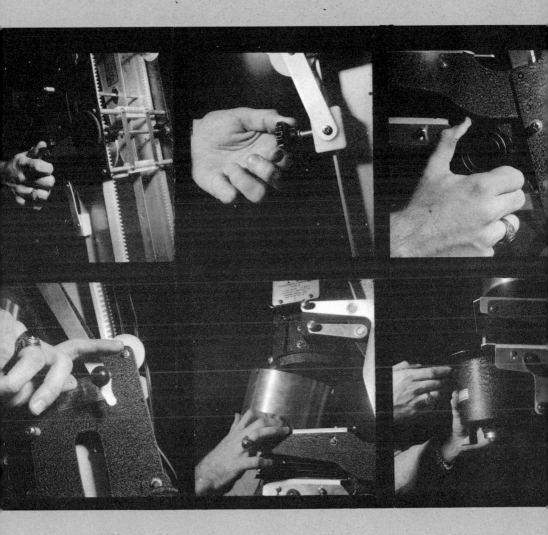

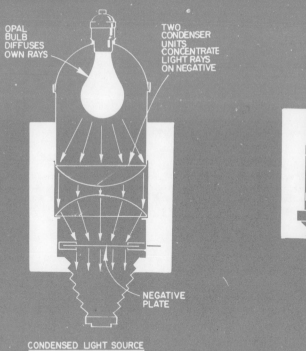

OPAL
BULB
DIFFUSES
OWN RAYS

TWO
CONDENSER
UNITS
CONCENTRATE
LIGHT RAYS
ON NEGATIVE

NEGATIVE
PLATE

CONDENSED LIGHT SOURCE

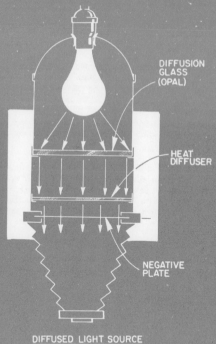

DIFFUSION
GLASS
(OPAL)

HEAT
DIFFUSER

NEGATIVE
PLATE

DIFFUSED LIGHT SOURCE

CIRCULAR FLUORESCENT TUBE

GRID TYPE CATHODE

OPAL
GLASS

NEGATIVE
PLATE

TWO TYPES OF COLD LIGHT SOURCE

Diagrams illustrate how light from standard opal enlarging bulb is transmitted through the negative to easel in condenser and diffusion enlargers. From a given enlarging bulb and lens aperture, a negative will require more exposure in diffusion enlarger but will have advantage of not projecting scratches or dust particles. Coldlight enlargers are generally of the two types illustrated. One big advantage of the coldlight enlarger is that it doesn't heat up, preventing "negative buckle."

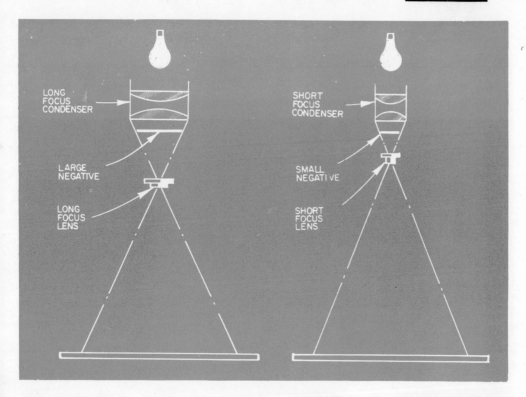

LONG FOCUS CONDENSER

LARGE NEGATIVE

LONG FOCUS LENS

SHORT FOCUS CONDENSER

SMALL NEGATIVE

SHORT FOCUS LENS

Long-focus condensers are required to distribute the light through a large negative, while short-focus condensers are used to collect and channel all the light through the whole area of smaller neg.

Cutaway view of DeJur shows coldlight set up for printing 35mm; note the recessed lensboard.

In most surfaces it is available in five grades of contrast, one more grade than most enlarging papers. It has a great range of exposure and development latitude. Blacks are consistent throughout all five grades, and the No. 5 grade is slightly less than fantastic. (See discussion of Kodabromide No. 5 in the Varigam chapter.) On it, prints are possible from negatives which would otherwise require time-consuming intensification to make even a passable print on grade 4.

Kodabromide grades:

No. 1   for negatives of high density
No. 2   for negatives of normal density
No. 3   for negatives of low density
No. 4   for negatives of very low density
No. 5   for negatives of extremely low density.

Dilute Dektol (or D-72 formula), 1 part stock solution to 2 parts water. The recommended developing time is 1½ minutes, while the useful range of the paper is from

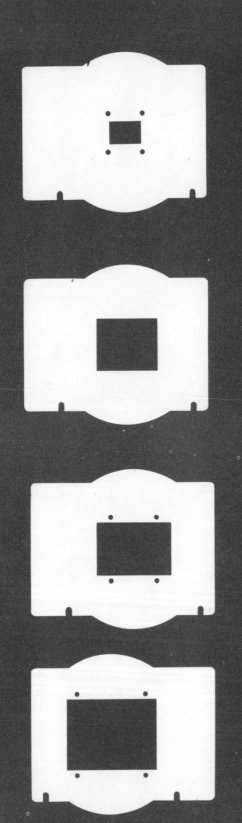

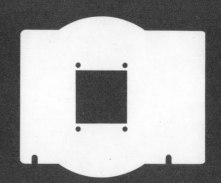

Omega D-2 and D-3 enlargers handle negs from 35mm to 4x5; two 4x5 neg carriers are shown in photo with a 35mm carrier. The 4x5 carrier at top of group is of universal type in that it has glass plates and can be used (with masks) for various-sized negatives. Illustrated, top to bottom, are 35mm, Omega 120 camera, $2\frac{1}{4}$x$3\frac{1}{4}$, $3\frac{1}{4}$x$3\frac{1}{4}$ carriers, and top right, the standard $2\frac{1}{4}$x$2\frac{1}{4}$ size.

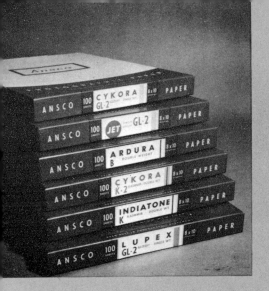

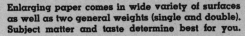

Enlarging paper comes in wide variety of surfaces as well as two general weights (single and double). Subject matter and taste determine best for you.

A paper safe is handy darkroom aid; weighted door is a genuine time-saver when measured against bother of motion required in opening boxes.

1 minute to 3 minutes. These times are for development at 68 degrees, and note that though a few degrees one way or the other won't ruin a print, because the controls are visual, the best results are obtained with 68 degrees working temperature. The use of Kodak Selectol developer will give somewhat warmer tones than Dektol, as desirable in some types of portraiture.

Kodabromide has one particular trait which you might not catch on to in years and years of infrequent use, and this is the fact that it "blackens" slightly upon hitting the hypo. This means that when you judge a Kodabromide print under the proper Wratten OA safelight you should mentally allow for this change when you estimate whether your print has developed far enough and has reached the right degree of tone.

Velour Black: Available in four grades of contrast, this chloro-bromide paper by Du Pont has an extremely wide latitude of development, thus permitting over- and underexposed prints to be saved through a change in the recommended developing time of 1½ minutes in 55-D (or use Kodak Dektol, as many professionals do with this paper).

If you want warm-tone results from Velour Black you need only increase the amount of potassium bromide in 55-D developer. The paper is available in the usual commercial surfaces such as glossy, matte, and semi-matte, plus a wide variety of salon and illustrators surfaces ranging all the way to silk finish. The fact that Velour Black is not quite as fast as Kodabromide does not seem to bother users of condenser enlargers. Velour Black does not undergo any visual change ("blackening") when immersed in hypo. Its single-weight varieties seem to be on a slightly heavier stock than Kodabromide, but whether this is desirable is a matter of personal taste—there must be *some* people who prefer a "thinner" paper.

Varigam: This paper is unusual in many, many ways. A lot of people like it and a lot plain don't. Now, of the latter group of don'ts there are a majority who have heard the name "Varigam" but have never tried the paper. They've heard it on the good authority of other photographers—who also have never used Varigam—that it couldn't be much good. The longer a photographer or professional photo-printer has been printing *without* Varigam, the harder it becomes to sell him on the fact that the Varigam approach to printing is a darn fine idea. We'll examine the pros and cons of Varigam variable contrast paper •

2155

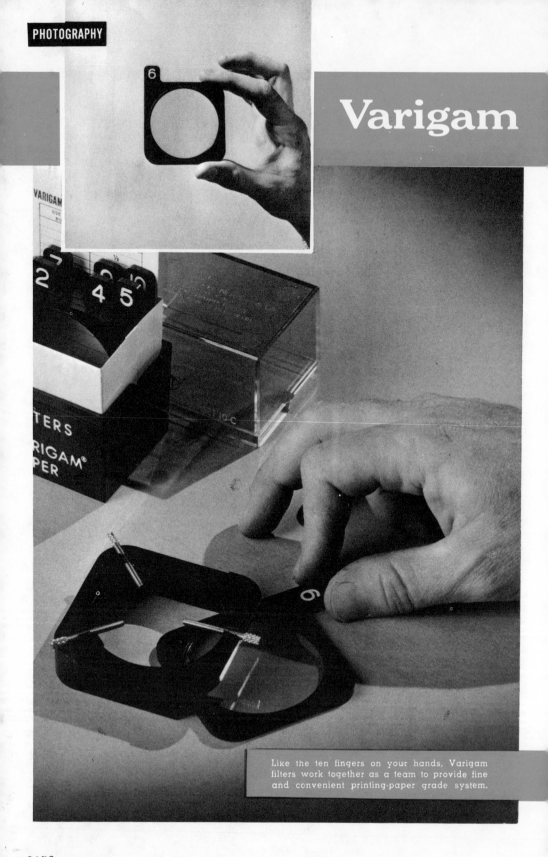

Varigam

Like the ten fingers on your hands, Varigam filters work together as a team to provide fine and convenient printing-paper grade system.

The choice of graded paper or Varigam is up to you, but here's what makes this combination of one paper and ten filters so popular today.

WHETHER you buy paper *other* than Varigam in packages of 10, boxes of 100, or the still more economical boxes of 500 sheets (a 500-sheet box costs about the same as four 100-sheet boxes, giving you 100 extra sheets for the same money if you make the single purchase), you still will have to buy a like quantity in each of four grades. For example, suppose you decide on 100-sheet boxes of grades No. 1, 2, 3, 4. You then have 400 sheets of paper to cover the various types of negatives which come along and which vary according to development and subject contrast. You're bound to use a few sheets from each box of paper, it is true—but actually you **are** limited to a maximum of 100 sheets of a given grade for whatever number of prints you can squeeze out. A 500-sheet box of Varigam, for the same money as your four 100-sheet boxes of different grades of standard enlarging paper, can be considered as 500 sheets of whatever grade you need at the flick of your wrist.

Need No. 2 paper? Fine, you've *got* No. 2 paper, all you need, through the use of the No. 5 Varigam filter. Need No. 3 paper? Easy: replace the No. 5 filter with the No. 7 Varigam filter and you've got No. 3 paper. All of these different grades of paper come from one box with the use of a Varigam filter under the lens of your enlarger. Furthermore, there are ten filters to cover the complete range of contrasts, permitting half-grades, or grades in-between the standard sequence of contrasts in all other enlarging paper. Actually, you can use Varigam to advantage with a set of just five filters—Nos. 1, 3, 5, 7 and 10—and when first starting with this paper it might make it easier to grasp. You can add the other five—Nos. 2, 4, 6, 8, 9—as you see a need for them. For example, the No. 6 gives a moderate difference in tone between what you'd get with the No. 5 (normal) and the No. 7 (medium). But it is important that you know what the No. 5 filter and No. 7 filter will do before deciding that what you want is No. 6, the half grade between "normal" and "medium." Experienced printers will soon see that better prints become easier!

At left is plastic filter holder that comes with 10-filter set; below is metal one for the Omega.

Anti-static solution also comes with 10-filter set, is used to make filters repel darkroom dust.

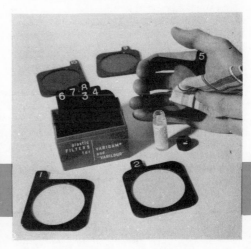

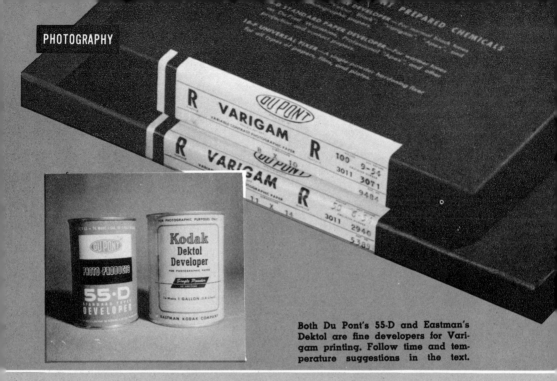

Both Du Pont's 55-D and Eastman's Dektol are fine developers for Varigam printing. Follow time and temperature suggestions in the text.

Varigam comes in two types, one plainly named Varigam and the other called High Speed Varigam. They cost the same, so we'll examine the two papers comparatively, and then the two of the Varigams against Kodabromide. Meanwhile, in case the discussion starts getting a little too deep for you, it might be a good idea to give the chapter *Making the Print* a quick preliminary reading.

Varigam was introduced in the U.S.A. in 1940, and before that in England. Originally there were but two filters, a yellow and a blue. The printer would then expose his sheet of Varigam enlarging paper according to the contrast he needed by using both filters successively but varying the percentage of exposure time through each.

An example of how this worked will best explain it: The blue filter is for the hard end of the scale and the yellow filter is for the soft end of the scale. Now, don't confuse this as meaning "hard negative" or "soft negative." A soft (or thin) negative requires the contrast to be in the paper to make up for its absence in the negative. A contrasty, or dense (heavy) negative often calls for a soft paper. Theoretically, a normal negative would be in the middle and therefore require 50% of the exposure time through the yellow filter and 50% remaining exposure time through the blue filter. For a harder (medium) paper you merely gave 70% exposure through the blue filter and 30% through the yellow.

Needless to say, the paper had amazing possibilities, but the two-filter system was somewhat complicated for amateur acceptance. Soon Varigam was made available with ten different filters covering the whole range of contrasts from very soft to moderately hard. The filters were made of gelatin and came in cardboard mounts which were to be slipped under the lens and above the enlarging paper. These, in turn, were replaced by durable optical plastic filters which are built to last longer than the ones of gelatin and cardboard. The point of this evolutionary history of Varigam is to trace back the hardships it has been up against in its fight for popular acceptance. Perhaps the reasons you haven't tried Varigam start back in the original two-filter days.

Before the introduction of High Speed Varigam there were many darkroom workers who declared that they liked the whole idea of Varigam except for the fact that it was too slow. This was somewhat true for those using old-style diffusion enlargers. High Speed was the answer, being twice the speed of regular Varigam. After you decide to give the Varigam idea a fair trial, your choice of *which* Varigam will be pretty much based on these factors:

Regular Varigam
1. When your enlarger is "fast" or a condenser model such as the Omega D-2.
2. If you prefer your negatives on the

thin side, as desirable with 35mm and 2¼x2¼. Regular Varigam runs almost a full grade harder with the No. 10 filter than High Speed, and thus is preferable for low-contrast miniature camera negatives.

3. To allow longer printing time, which permits more for balanced, effective dodging and burning-in.

High Speed Varigam

1. When your enlarger is "slow" (usually a model of the diffusion type).
2. To reduce enlarging exposure when making extreme blowups of small sections of a negative, since exposure time multiplies as the negative carrier rides away from the baseboard.
3. If your negatives are the larger sizes (4x5, for example) or you tend to develop your negatives to a greater degree of contrast.
4. To reduce exposure time on production runs.

Relationship of Varigam to Graded Papers

Paper contrast....	Soft	Normal	Medium	Hard
Kodabromide	1	2	3	4
Varigam filters	1,2,3	4,5,6	7,8	9,10

In the case of Kodabromide there is one additional grade of contrast not listed on the chart. This is grade 5 and it is not always on the shelf of every photo-supply house. For one thing, there aren't many calls for it; and for another, aged No. 5 paper tends to print softer than fresh paper. Buy Kodabromide 5 paper in small quantities only and pay special attention to expiration date if you intend commanding it to work a miracle and make your otherwise unprintable negative into a thing of beauty.

Somewhere along the line, photographers worked up the notion that it is a horrible crime even to print on No. 4 paper, and that the ultimate is a normal negative that prints on paper called "normal." This notion usually arises from a guilt complex resulting from negative underexposure or underdevelopment or a combination of both. Flat, lifeless negatives resulting from outdated film generally call for 4 paper. Photographers never really like the prints they get on 4 paper because there was usually something wrong with the negative before it was even put into the enlarger.

Five paper, even less in general use, is capable of delivering a good print from a "miserable" negative (but before you read

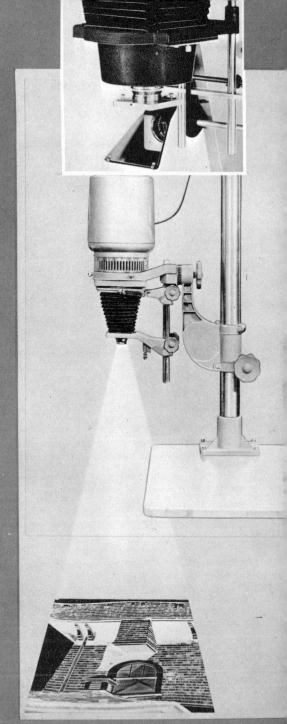

Two techniques for bigger-than-baseboard enlargements are shown above; here is where High Speed Varigam is useful to reduce long exposure times. Top inset is Omega's right-angle projection accessory. Beneath, DeJur enlarger rotates on its vertical column to project big image onto floor.

f.11, 4 seconds

f.16, 4 seconds

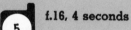

f.11, 4 seconds

5 **f.11, 4 seconds**

Scene is Grand Hotel lobby, Paris. Negative is normal; the large print was made on High Speed Varigam paper through the No. 5 filter

f.8, 4 seconds **5**

Exposure for the large print, as noted, was f.11 at 4 seconds; a 212 enlarging bulb was used in the author's ten-year-old D-2 Omega. Development was two full minutes in 68-degree Dektol. Same data applies to surrounding prints with differences of diaphragm opening and Varigam filter noted. The point: proper exposure time and proper filter are equally important factors in making a good print; it is best to determine the correct enlarging exposure of a filter before resorting to switching to other filters. See suggestions on test strips in Making the Print.

any further about the use and treatment of No. 5 paper, it'd be wise to reread the chapter on developing the negative, where we say that a good print starts with a good negative) and is, perhaps a timesaver for the photographer who doesn't want to bother with intensification. He forgets that the contrastier papers (Kodabromide in this example) have a shorter scale and consequently render fewer varied tones between black and white. If you use exhausted developer on your film, No. 5 paper can save your life. It can produce prints for the photographer who doesn't bother to check his temperature in the winter, and who gets flat, thin negatives from too-cold developer. Five paper cannot put things into a negative which the film never had a chance to record (as in the case of underexposure or faulty flash synchronization), but it can help you get a better print from what's left!

So when you hear photo-printers complain, "I like Varigam but it doesn't go hard enough for all types of negatives," you should conclude that this is an okeh statement from a laboratory which has to print everything that comes along—but in *your* case it is a poor excuse. Get a package of Kodabromide 5 to supplement (i.e. extend the range of) your 500 sheets of Varigam. You'll likely print through a second 500-sheet box of Varigam before you even open the No. 5. Better yet, make negatives which are far away from this fringe area.

Without any of the filters, both Varigam and High Speed Varigam print as a normal paper, similar to grade 2 in Kodabromide or Velour Black. High Speed Varigam triples its own speed without any filters. Regular Varigam doubles its speed (half the enlarging exposure time) without its filters. As an example of how this works, consider a negative that calls for a No. 5 filter. Whatever the proper exposure is to make this print, you can make an exact duplicate in tone and contrast without the No. 5 filter by reducing the enlarging exposure time one half with regular Varigam and by two thirds with High Speed Varigam.

The High Speed with filters is about the same speed as Velour Black, while the regular with filters would require double the exposure of Velour Black at the No. 5 filter level. This is something to keep in mind when you need extra speed from either regular or High Speed Varigam, as in the cases of extreme blowups or production runs from normal printing negatives. This all leads into another advantage of both the

Varigams, and that is continuity in exposure times. Here is how this works:

When we refer to grades of paper, as in the Velour Black or Kodabromide lines, we assign a number or name to the paper as related to the amount of exposure necessary to give the blackest blacks and the whitest whites in direct relation to the content of the negative being printed. Each grade of paper, while a member of the same brand-name family, offers a separate solution to the problem of proper print contrast. If, after repeated trials, you decide that your negatives won't make a satisfactory print on normal (grade 2) paper, the next step is to ask yourself *why*. One answer might be that the resulting print looked "soft" and that it didn't have clear whites or true blacks. Next thing you do is try the medium paper (grade 3) and the whole process starts over again. The exposure time established for the print projected on normal paper has no bearing on the exposure time for the print to be made on medium paper—except that it will be *different*. Harder papers require more time than normal paper, but the rule is meaningless as such; you never do find out the proper time for a good print on *normal* paper, as it can't be done because of the lack of contrast in the negative.

With Varigam paper, however, after you have determined the printing time, either through a test strip or photo-electric device, and you find the contrast of the resulting print is not to your liking, then you need only change filters, and not the exposure time. This will hold true for filters No. 1 through No. 8; a 20% increase in exposure time will be necessary for the No. 9 and No. 10 filters, which transmit less light due to their dark, bluish colors. This knowledge should be of great value in learning to judge exposure time and differences in contrast, and enable you to produce more prints than test strips. An effective and convincing test would be to print one of your better negatives through the No. 4, No. 5 and No. 6 filters. Use the same exposure time for all three prints and develop them together. Do not expect extreme variations as these filters are but a half-grade apart: these are differences you'll appreciate more and more as you come to regard yourself as a maker-of-fine-prints.

To demonstrate how the filters make a difference in contrast while the exposure times are constant, use this same negative for three more exposures, this time through No. 3, No. 5 and No. 7 filters. Naturally you will have to determine beforehand the proper exposure for the normal negative

through the No. 5 filter to derive any benefit from this comparative test. Again, use the same exposure time for all three prints and develop them together. Needless to say, the No. 5 filtered print is just right. The No. 3 filtered print will be properly exposed but will be soft and won't have the rich blacks characteristic of Varigam. The print through the No. 7 filter will also have correct exposure, but it will appear harder than the No. 5 printing—perhaps too hard to be considered acceptable.

These two simple tests show that it is certainly easier to lift filters around rather than boxes of paper. Further, it shows the continuity of exposure present in Varigam. With separately graded papers, three different exposure times would be necessary to produce comparable examples of contrast difference. And if you think that you'll never have occasion to print in this situation, bear in mind that you owe it to yourself, in terms of time, darkroom space and paper expense, to make the best possible print on the grade of paper you start with before deciding that a different grade is required. Even if you make a fairly good print on a given grade of paper and have some slight doubt about it, it is easier, far easier, to shift a filter rather than start anew with a graded paper that requires a different over-all basic exposure.

One thing that needs emphasis, relating to the use of Varigam, is: Please, please, use the manufacturer's recommended developing time of 2-2½ minutes. Use it with Dektol or 55-D, as you choose, but use this developing time *consistently*. Many workers prefer 53-D with Varigam to obtain prints with richer blacks. Remember this time—2-2½ minutes—as though it were treasured information from a fifty-dollar scratch sheet. The reason that graded papers allow variance in their developing times is because that is their method of control, that is how the tone can be varied within a given grade of paper. The disadvantage of this control method in graded paper is that you'll find yourself using the developing margin to offset errors of enlarging exposure—which makes for further confusion in jumping from one grade of paper to the next.

Hot water is often used to force "color" or tone into the lighter areas of a print which didn't respond during exposure. An example of this might be one of your flash negatives where there was a face very close to the camera. Most of the negative is developing nicely on No. 2 paper, but that face, oh that face, is so chalky white you can't make out who it is. You make another

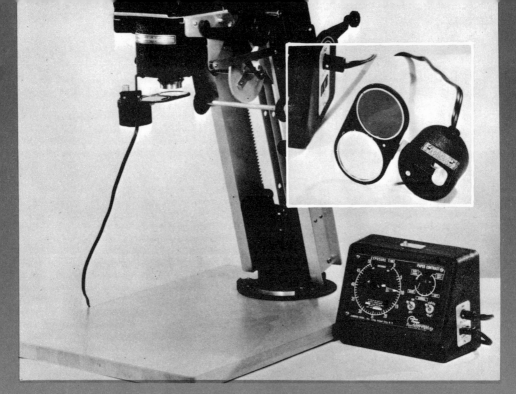

Ultimate in enlarger luxury is autofocusing Omega with new Electronic Variable Contrast Timer which selects filters, times exposures automatically. This accessory indicates multi-grade paper is here to stay.

print and you burn in the face, giving perhaps four times the exposure you are allowing the rest of the print. Still it doesn't do too well—so you use hot water to help it along. Or some printers might use undiluted developer which had been warmed slightly. What you really wish is that you could print part of the negative on No. 2 paper and print the face on No. 1 paper. With Varigam you'd merely do your burning-in through the No. 1 or No. 2 filter, and this would make the dense area print softer. Hot water? Not really necessary with Varigam.

There are printers who like to develop prints for 4 minutes, seemingly to build additional contrast into their graded-paper prints. Varigam is at its best at 2-2½ minutes, as mentioned earlier. It can be developed for less time and satisfactory prints will result. Longer developing times won't ruin it. But since its main advantage is in its variable contrast via filtering, it would be downright dumb not to take advantage of this. The advantages of a constant developing time plus known continuity of exposures certainly simplifies enlarging.

Because Varigam is yellow-green sensitive it requires a special safelight filter. This is the Du Pont S-55X, which is orange-brown in color, slightly different from the Wratten OA you would use for most other enlarging papers. Its relative darkness isn't real hardship, and once in use you'll soon stop comparing it with other safelights or other colors. With this S-55X safelight you have one safelight suitable for all paper. Many printers maintain that the S-55X enables them better to judge the related tones of blacks and near-blacks. Re variety in the blacks, it should be noted that Varigam lends itself very nicely to ferricyanide touch-up which, unlike on the graded papers, is not easy to discern.

Varigam and its kissin' cousin, Varilour, are the U.S. forerunners of a long line of variable contrast papers coming onto the market. (Varilour is the warm-toned version of the all-around Varigam discussed here.) From another direction the Omega enlarger people have an approach to variable contrast printing which overcomes the occasional objections to changing filters. It goes by the long name of Electronic Variable Contrast Timer, and by setting a knob and a dial you select your filter and the exposure time, which starts at the press of a button. It will make variable contrast papers easier to use should you have some mental block against the changing of filters. Actually, Varigam is quite easy to use and it makes sense. •

What's a Good Print?

You can only generalize about a phrase like "good composition." However, good technique is something else: you have to know how.

WHEN we use the expression "print quality," what do we mean? Can it be described on paper in a book? It can; it is the tangible result of mastering of the printing technique with a healthy mixture of "proper attitude." Don't move on to the next negative to be printed until you have done your very best on the one now in the enlarger. Proper contrast in your print and pleasing composition are both quite important when you strive for good print quality.

Enlarging allows a second chance at composition, an opportunity to refine and correct that which you've done in making the negative. Don't think of enlarging composition, however, as an excuse and cure-all for sloppy camera work. It isn't! Enlarging allows you to emphasize certain areas of your picture and to minimize others. A photographer who is a good printer soon learns to think in terms of a finished print at the time he is taking his picture. This means that, for example, he'll learn to avoid areas of extreme brightness when making a low-key picture (as the case of an open window with bright

sunlight pouring into a softly lit natural-light scene taken indoors).

In taking your pictures do not overlook the factors of lightness and darkness in your picture arrangement, or "composition." If you have no control over these, at least try to position them at the extreme of the negative so that they can be cropped or burned in more easily when necessary. One of the most widely used methods of holding eye interest within the area of the print is the darkening of corners. Conversely, the use of sky-darkening filters can be a simple method of emphasizing subject matter.

Don't be afraid of the term "composition." There has been so much hokum published on the subject of good composition that the amateur photographer is often so preoccupied with composition that he forgets to include *human interest* in his photographs.

Even if you are a relative newcomer in the photographic hobby or profession it is likely that you have heard some talk about triangular highlights on cheeks in portraits, and that landscape scenes always contain a triangle or an S-curve. Perhaps you've seen some of the print critics at an amateur salon fawning over a print in which the horizon was placed at the exact "one-third or two-thirds from the top" position. The judges were checking the print with a ruler and it was awarded a green ribbon. The fact that it was a miserable photograph had little bearing on the prize, and perhaps you even wondered why the guy bothered to dry the print after he'd made

At right, translucent Fiberglas and an overcast day combine to make a tough picture-taking situation. Special attention was paid to pattern made by hands so as to present idea that Fiberglas is so thin that light can pass through. Face would be distracting unless it were allowed to go dark. Photographed for U. S. Rubber by author Simon Nathan, photo was printed on Varigam. In photo at left, L-shaped cardboard cropping guides are useful for planning best possible composition for enlargement.

it. This is exactly the point: compose and print your picture to please the eye. Place the center of interest where it will be easy to locate with the trained scanning motion of the human eye, which is, just as you read these words, across the page from left to right. Faces should not be looking out of the picture, or the viewer of the print will find himself also looking away to the right or to the left to see what the subject of the picture is looking at. Try to have your subject matter entering the picture rather than leaving it; otherwise it gives the impression that you shot too late or should have turned your camera a bit in the direction the subject matter is going or looking. These, however, are generalized suggestions, not hard-and-fast rules.

There are many, many things you can do to make your prints (and treatment of subject matter) more effective. Try reversing the negative. This means placing it in the enlarger with the emulsion away from the enlarging paper. Refocusing will be necessary (in the case of an autofocus Omega you need only turn the manual focusing over-ride control). When reversing a negative in an effort to make a composition more pleasing to the eye it is wise not to use a negative containing signs or numbers of any kind as they, too, will be reversed and prove distracting. In portraiture, the handkerchief in the breast pocket of a man's suit may be a slight problem. Try to crop it out or to burn it in dark enough that it won't be distracting.

Marked contact sheet at left shows which negatives are to be printed and how they are to be cropped. Crop marks serve to eliminate unimportant areas that don't tell story. Scenes are at Indianapolis race when Bill Vukovitch was killed.

Compose pictures of people so that they are looking into the center of print area. At right, book in pilot's hand is somewhat distracting since it draws eye away from main subject. By burning in this light area, the print could be improved.

Learn that you can often simplify your picture and make its content more effective merely by raising the enlarging head and eliminating extraneous matter. In fancier language this is known as cropping, and it's a good technique to keep in mind.

There are two main schools of thought on this cropping-composition idea. First one is that you should contact-print your negatives and then mark the area to be enlarged. This can be done loosely with a grease pencil to indicate the general area to be enlarged. It can also be done with a sliding mask, marked to give in miniature the proportions of the popular sizes of enlarging paper, usually 5x7, 8x10, and 11x14. Needless to say, 35mm users will hardly be able to crop on their contact prints unless they make enlarged contact sheets. The main advantage of contact printing before enlarging is in the case of multiple exposures where the selection of the best action or expression will be the important factor in determining which negative to enlarge.

Second school of thought is that contact printing for reference during enlarging is a waste of time, and that by looking at your negatives in the enlarged condition you'll see many more points to be corrected, eliminated, and emphasized. And ask a busy professional about composition. Almost for sure, he'll brush you with "who's got time for composition?" He'll tell you that he shoots and prints to make his pictures "look good." •

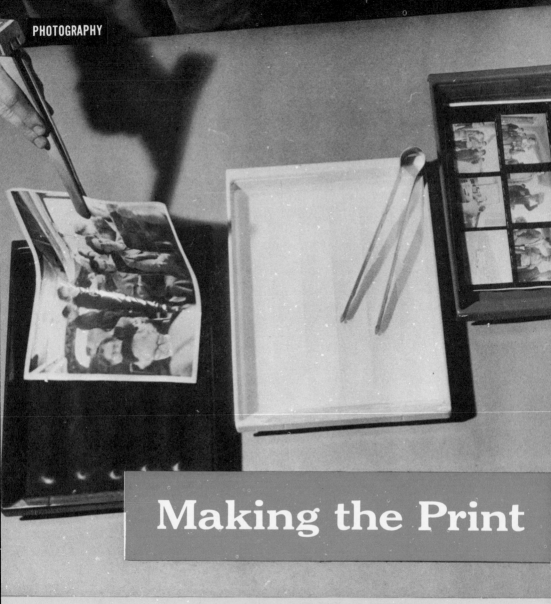

Making the Print

ALL the effort you have put into the taking of your picture—the right camera, the proper film, the correct exposure, development of the negative to normal contrast, everything—will soon be coordinated into a finished result, an enlargement! It's based on this enlargement that your stock will rise or fall in the eyes of those who see your picture. Too soft a print can obscure detail. Too hard a print may cause the eye to jump from point to point, missing a lot of the beauty still buried in your negative. Learn to make better enlargements and people will say that you are a better photographer. Excuses require almost the same effort as

good technique, and accomplish very little.

With the enlarger light on, raise the condenser above the negative carrier and look for dust and dirt on your negative. The advantage of cleaning the negative in its carrier, with the carrier in the enlarger, are (1) it is easier to see the dust and (2) once you've cleaned the negative there is little likelihood of dust returning. (Dusting the negative carrier outside of the enlarger and then moving it into position can attract dust.) Use a soft camel's-hair brush for dusting. A product called Photo-Sweep, sprayed ever so lightly from the self-pressured can, will make your negative dust-repellent; when the treated nega-

Time spent removing dust from negatives is time saved when it comes to spotting. One method, shown below left, is to use a Staticmaster brush. Another, below, right, is use of an anti-static spray plus camel's-hair brush.

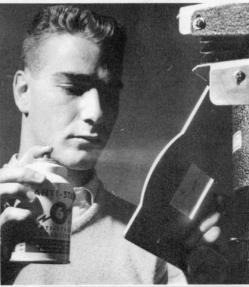

You need to learn which grades of paper suit your negatives, how to control development temperature and run test strips.

tive is brushed the free dirt and dust sweeps right off. For dirt that is stuck to the negative, use a dab of carbon tetrachloride on a piece of clean, long-fiber cotton. After the top of the negative is clean, lift the negative carrier without removing it from the enlarger and brush off the negative as necessary. Time spent in making the negative clean comes back many-fold through time saved in not having to spot your enlargements. Fifteen or twenty seconds cleaning the negative, before you make even the first test strip, should become standard operating procedure. (The specific procedural instructions above are for author's Omega D-2.)

Next, open the lens, to its maximum aperture, usually f.4.5, and compose your picture on the easel. Cropping is important, so don't rush at this point. Is there something you can do to make your picture more effective? Is there something distracting in the foreground? If it is a square negative, will you print it as a vertical or a horizontal? If it is a 35mm negative, which end will you crop to make a standard 8x10 enlargement?

Intended use can help you answer the question of what size print to make. Is the print destination an album, a wall, or a small dresser easel? Print size is determined best by viewing distance. Generally,

5x7's and 8x10's make up the bulk of enlarging production, as they give the right perspective when held in the hand at a normal, relaxed arm's length. Size 11x14 is for somewhat more distant viewing and is certainly the maximum size the average two eyes can encompass without a step backward. Also, 11x14's are fine for wall display in the home, especially when accented on a 16x20 mount. For an album, it is nice to vary the sizes and make the more important pictures larger, and make desirable but less important pictures smaller.

Whatever the size, the first thing you'll do after you compose your subject matter on the easel is to check for critical focus. This can be done either by bending over and putting your eye close to the image on the easel or with a reflex ground-glass focusing device. The latter is desirable in that it allows you to see the focusing process up to and beyond the sharpest point, much easier than naked-eye examination of the image reflected from the white surface of the enlarging easel.

Next, stop down the lens—but not for the same reasons that you stopped down your camera lens when taking the picture. At the camera, lens aperture points serve (1) to control the amount of light that reaches the film (that is, as an exposure variable to balance a selected shutter speed) and (2) as a means of increasing or decreasing depth of field. Stopping down the enlarging lens after accurately focusing the negative on the easel won't cause your negative to print any sharper. Good enlarging lenses are designed to cover a flat field from edge to edge. However, a wide-open enlarging lens, even on the slowest of enlarging papers, would require an exposure so short that neither you nor the electronic timer assisting you could switch the enlarger bulb on and off in time. An enlarging exposure of, for example, a theoretical ½ second would be hard to reckon with. How in the world are you going to reduce ½ second by, say, 20%? It's even harder to figure out mathematically, than to do.

The logical thing to do is to have a printing exposure time that will be long enough to permit measured variations of at least 1 second in time. A moderately long exposure might be desired if you have a large amount of burning-in and dodging to perform. On the other hand, prolonged exposures invite enlarger vibration and heat damage to your negative. Only the years can teach you when this exception will apply. Ten seconds is a good time to shoot for because it is easy to calculate exposure changes by percentage in whole

seconds: e.g., a 20% decrease in overall exposure changes the 10 seconds to 8 seconds. For example: On the Omega D-2 with the 212 enlarging bulb, using a 2¼x2¼ negative, 90mm lens, with 3½-inch condensers in place, you can figure an average exposure for 8x10 through the No. 5 filter on High Speed Varigam at f.16 and 10 seconds with a normal negative. (The noted High Speed Varigam and 212 bulb combination, as used by the author, offers the advantage of a brighter—150 watt—light for focusing.) For regular Varigam, f.11 and 10 seconds would be a good starting point. The use of shorter, faster exposures leaves less margin for exposure error and less time to do any worthwhile dodging. The 10-second basic time also allows you to figure the two-filter Varigam technique more easily. Needless to say, if you have a lot of prints to make and the negative doesn't require too much manipulation, it'd be wise to open up the lens to a larger aperture and reduce the exposure time in direct ratio.

Making the Test Strip

Whatever the basic exposure time works out to be in your particular combination of Omega condensers, varied focal length lenses, regular Varigam or High Speed Varigam, with or without filters, don't overlook the importance of a *test strip,* as this is the means by which you take a sample print from a small section of the negative area. An 8x10 sheet of paper makes four suitable test strips, each 2¼x8 inches. Anything smaller is false economy as it would really be too small for the range of an average negative enlarged to 8x10 inches, and it would be expensive timewise. The idea is to place the long, narrow strip of enlarging paper across the more important areas of your enlargement. This should include, whenever possible, the light and the dark areas so that when you develop the test strip you'll see (1) how close you are to correct exposure and (2) the relationship of the contrasts on the grade of paper (or Varigam filter) you've selected.

The Kodak projection print scale is one of the finest devices for determining correct exposure time. It is a sheet of film that you place over a piece of enlarging paper (for this, tear your 8x10 sheet into four 4x5 sections) on the easel and expose with the negative to be enlarged. It requires 1 full minute exposure, and when developed it will show the segments, each with a different density and a number. The section that appears to have the best tone will be easily determined visually. Read the number in terms of seconds and you'll have the correct exposure. This method does not judge contrast, so don't think of it as a substitute for the test strip, but more as an aid when making extreme blowups or when using an enlarging paper with which you are not familiar. It can be a time-saver and paper-saver in the switch from Varigam to Kodabromide No. 5 in those rare cases when you may need it.

In an accompanying illustration you see a perfectly exposed print with the test strip subtracted from the center section. This is done as a suggestion as to placement of a test strip, as well as to show the relationship of proper timing of the test with the finished enlargement. Important to remember is, develop your test strip the full time called for by the type of enlarging paper and developer you are using. Your test may tell you that the time is correct, and with full development you can see that the contrast of the print is not. With Varigam, it is relatively simple to select another filter for a correction of contrast without the necessity of a new timing trial. Note that a wet print will *appear* to be somewhat more contrasty than a dry print.

It is not to be expected that all negatives will print on "normal" paper (or Varigam No. 5 filter): the normal condition is primarily a mean condition from which we go just "softer than" and "harder than." Type of illumination, contrast of subject matter, and the nature of the negative development itself are the determining factors in fitting a negative to a specific grade of paper. The ideal condition would be to have 35mm and roll negatives developed so that most of them would print on normal paper, thus allowing a wider margin for encompassing subjects and lighting conditions which fall on both sides of average. Examine the negatives reproduced here and their resulting prints on different grades of paper. By matching your negatives to this group you can see what paper is appropriate.

Do not be satisfied with the first prints you make, but make additional ones at different contrast for the main purpose of comparison. What looks fine alone may not appear so perfect alongside moderate variations in tone. By comparisons you can learn faster what is good and what is just passable. This judgment in the darkroom will prove to be every bit as important as selecting the right camera, film, background, and even, as they say around the art museums, "the exact instant." All of your photographic talents with the camera won't be worth the effort if you don't sum them up in a fine print.

Before making your test strip make sure that your print developer is very near the

Heathkit timer illustrated is a do-it-yourself job which comes in kit form and is easily assembled. It times prints accurately with exposures of one second to one minute, pays off in paper saving.

The Bausch and Lomb enlarging focusing magnifier is a valuable darkroom accessory for the critical focusing of negatives. Its highly magnified image serves the photographer by reducing eyestrain.

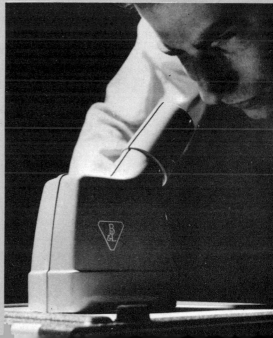

recommended 68- to 70-degree working temperature. It is true that you can make prints at just about any temperature since the controls are visual; but to obtain the maximum in tonal range from your enlarging paper, don't start compromising quality before you have even developed as little as one test strip. In hot weather a small jar of ice cubes placed in the developer in one corner of the tray will help keep the temperature down. Running water under the developing tray is a simple arrangement if you can play your developing tray in a larger tray containing the circulating water. Winter time the same tray-in-a-tray arrangement might prove necessary

to bring the temperature up—however, the cold tap water will require a blend of hot water; check it with your thermometer. And as mentioned in the Darkroom chapter, a good circulation of fresh or even chilled air makes summer darkroom work more bearable.

Develop the test strip and look at it after it has been in the hypo about a minute. Turn on your white light, and if you see that the test-strip print has a yellowish cast it indicates that the print is not completely fixed. Return it to the hypo for another 30 to 60 seconds. If the strip still isn't free of the faint yellow cast, the hypo isn't working properly. This means that it is too weak if

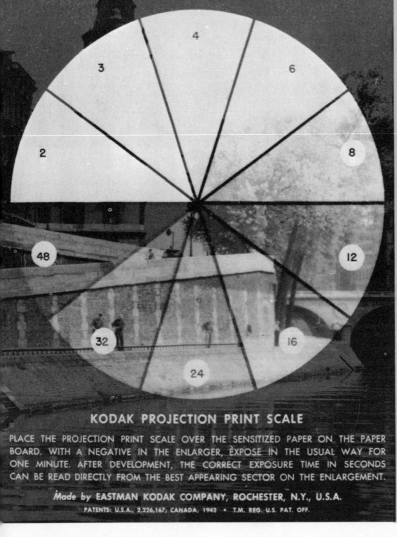

KODAK PROJECTION PRINT SCALE

PLACE THE PROJECTION PRINT SCALE OVER THE SENSITIZED PAPER ON THE PAPER BOARD. WITH A NEGATIVE IN THE ENLARGER, EXPOSE IN THE USUAL WAY FOR ONE MINUTE. AFTER DEVELOPMENT, THE CORRECT EXPOSURE TIME IN SECONDS CAN BE READ DIRECTLY FROM THE BEST APPEARING SECTOR ON THE ENLARGEMENT.

Made by EASTMAN KODAK COMPANY, ROCHESTER, N.Y., U.S.A.

PATENTS: U.S.A., 2,226,167; CANADA, 1942 • T.M. REG. U.S. PAT. OFF.

Print Scale is a useful device for determining exposure time and also shows what relative exposure times will look like. Once you understand the potentialities of the paper you're using you'll substitute the technique shown on the opposite page. However, don't discard your scale as it is useful when experimenting with a different type of printing paper or working on an unfamiliar enlarger.

Print at top shows difference between eight, six, four and two seconds exposure. This was done by moving a sheet of cardboard from left to right in four two-second exposures. Center photo shows actual placement of test strip so that it covers range of negative from shadows to brightest point. This is the most efficient and economical method. Bottom print is the correct exposure, six seconds, and matches the second from left test panel illustrated in the top example.

it is fresh solution, or that it is exhausted. The use of an acetic-acid short stop bath between the developer and hypo immediately stops the action of the developer, neutralizing or eliminating the alkali, and reducing the demands on the hypo solution and thus prolonging its useful life. Acetic acid and hypo are discussed in the following chapter.

Judging the Test Strip

Assuming that you have a recognizable image on the test strip we'll examine it to determine how we'll proceed. If the test strip is black it means that there was many times the necessary exposure—or, plainly, "too much." If it is white, or with faint traces of gray where the black should appear, then the exposure was far from sufficient—or plainly, "not enough."

Study the values in your test strip. Are the blacks truly black? Are the whites really white, or are they overcast and somewhat gray? Is the contrast between the blacks and the whites extreme? Are there many middle tones? And remember, this analysis presupposes your having completed the full developing time in each case.

If extreme blacks and whites are present it means that your paper is of too high contrast for the negative being printed. Use the next grade softer for your next test, and in the case of Varigam, skip down two filter numbers (say, from No. 7 to No. 5) and try it again.

If the blacks never actually blacken, even with full development, you can conclude that you are using too soft a paper, or that you haven't given sufficient over-all exposure time. Before you change Varigam filters or grades of papers, make a second test strip with an increase in exposure.

If the whites are veiled with gray you can assume that your exposure is too long or that the paper is too soft. In this case a decrease in over-all exposure is advised for a high-contrast enlarging paper.

You really should come close to the correct enlarging exposure, using the Kodak projection print scale, before trying to determine the correct contrast. Varigam will save you a number of test strips because of its continuity of exposure though all numbers of the filters, plus a known 20% increase in exposure for the No. 9 and No. 10 filters; use it for a while if you are just starting with a new enlarger.

Following the test to determine the proper time and proper contrast, you are ready to make a print on a full-sized sheet of enlarging paper. Do not expect perfec-

Temperature of the developer is very important in print developing. Look at the example above and larger reproduction at the right. Believe it or not, but both were made through the same No. 5 Varigam filter, five seconds exposure at f.11 and developed two minutes in Dektol developer. But the print above was developed in 58° developer and one at right in 68°. Increasing the exposure in too-cold developer as much as five times will not produce quality obtained in proper temperature.

tion, even though you have the right contrast and right enlarging exposure time. Rare, rare indeed, is the negative that will yield a perfect straight print. It is almost axiomatic that prints from any and every negative can be improved through dodging and burning-in of specific areas. But go ahead and make the first straight print. Over-all, it looks fine—but if only you could see some more detail in the shadow area! You can, by reducing the amount of exposure given the shadowed area, through "dodging."

Left, ice in the tray can be used to reduce warm developer to the proper working range. Heavy-weight balloons filled with water and kept in refrigerator can also be used, or try running-water technique.

Above is seen the print tong mark caused by holding print to the safelight for a prolonged time during development. In case the mark is hypo-caused, just be more patient and give the print a chance to clear. The obvious remedy for the first situation is to relocate safelight closer to tray before continuing.

A chipped enamel tray may be easily, if not artistically, repaired with ordinary nailpolish. Enamel chips when solutions are allowed to crystallize (below right). Avoid this by rinsing trays carefully.

If most of your picture area is to be printed in terms of blacks and almost-blacks, it might be a good idea to set the over-all exposure so the blacks print without dodging and the whites will require burning-in. This is hard to pinpoint in words, but the idea is that both exposures will be known lengths of time. The highlights may require an additional three times the amount of the over-all exposure: exposure for blacks 4 seconds, exposure for white 12 seconds. In each case you have but to set your electric timer for 4 seconds, press once for over-all exposure, and then shade all but the highlight-white areas. (To "shade" is to prevent light from hitting the areas of black, which for sake of example we've set as a major part of the picture.) For the highlights we trigger our Time-O-Lite three times rather than reset it. If you have to employ this method too regularly, you may be developing too much contrast into your negatives.

Quite a number of professional darkroom men prefer the contortions of exposure for highlights: the impressive wiggling of the hands and dodger through the shadow areas during the over-all exposure. But that's just because they never sat down and thought it out.

In the event that you can't get the whites to print out with even a faint gray, you can aid the cause with Kodabromide by applying hot water, or warm diluted developer or stock developer to the unresponsive area. Variations of these are the application of hot breath or the heel of the hand, the idea being that this way you might not have to go back and make a properly exposed print. These methods are also worth knowing about (in the case of graded papers) when you are on the last sheet to your name of a particular grade.

If you have a negative with a dense area you can, in addition to the burning-in technique, give an over-all exposure of the Varigam print through the proper filter and then drop to a much lower filter for burning in the stubborn area. The two-filter technique with Varigam gives you a tremendous choice of grades of paper for a single negative. It is a technique worth mastering—and if you've never done it before or never thought of it before, be warned that a new Varigam user will tend to see every negative as a two-filter-printer and consequently find himself overdoing it (but not wrongly), somewhat in the manner of the printer who buys a deluxe set of dodging sticks in the camera store. Varigam's two-filter technique will actually help you in your picture-taking because, as we stated before, a good printer will think in terms of the print at the time he exposes the negative. And with graded papers he knows the limitations of each grade and the problems of jumping from grade to grade; he also knows there are numerous lighting situations to avoid, lest they become difficult or impossible to print. But with Varigam the photographer knows or soon learns that he can "get more out of his negative and onto the paper" than the users

Best agitation is achieved by lifting print out of developer and turning it over as seen below left. The emulsion is especially soft at this time. But never poke the middle of your print with the tong.

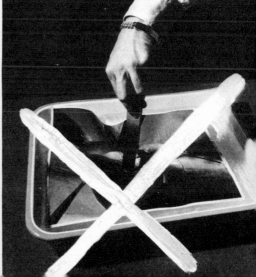

Negatives which appear contrasty, as in the case of this overexposed Miami Beach sunlight shot taken on Tri-X, print best on soft papers—use No. 1 in graded papers or No. 1, 2, 3 Varigam filters.

Normal negatives print best on grade 2 paper or through Varigam filters Nos. 4, 5, 6. Sky was filtered with 23a (orange) filter. Refer to Varigam chapter for how papers can affect normal negative.

Insufficient exposure left negative so thin that it needs printing on contrasty paper, No. 4, or with Nos. 9 and 10 Varigam filters. Separate face from background.

Medium paper, No. 3, or Varigam through Nos. 7 and 8 filters handles negatives which appear as above. They are too thin to print on normal paper, too dense for harder No. 4 papers. Developer wasn't replenished.

At right is faint image resulting from underdevelopment. There was sufficient light for f.3.5 exposure at 1/50th and film was properly exposed. Here, now, is a film which would print well on grade 5 paper.

Circus scene was printed from unpromising-looking negative shown in previous illustration. It was done without intensification to demonstrate what Kodabromide 5 can do.

of the regular unfiltered enlarging papers.

Take the specific problem of printing a negative—good, bad or indifferent—from which you need a print for reproduction, a print for a salesman's manual, plus a print for hanging in the reception room of the client. With Varigam and its half grades and continuity of exposure you can execute this order in jig time. However, given the above requirements and using regular graded papers you will find that it may take more manipulating (hot water, warm developer, a tiring expense in hot breath, and perhaps ferricyanide, to cover the lack of an intermediate grade of paper) and considerably more time. •

Short Stop,

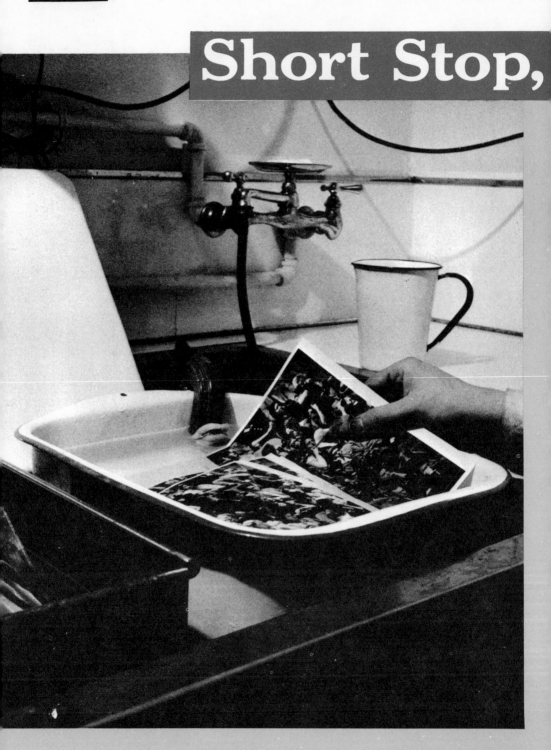

Running water alone is not enough to get hypo out of prints. Prints should be circulated, shuffled, agitated so that each gets a good wash. Constant movement by hand for 15 minutes is better than 2-hour soak.

Hypo and Wash

Too little attention often is given to these "mechanical" processes. Don't ruin your best print efforts by lazy neglect of the fundamentals.

A CASUAL mention of acetic acid has been made before, but its importance and usefulness should be emphasized. It stops the action of the developer and saves the hypo from this effort, leaving the hypo's strength to be applied toward clearing and hardening the print. Following is a useful table: From it determine which strength you want to buy and then standardize the amounts you'll use each time you enlarge, noting down the quantities on the wall, or painting them with red nail polish directly onto the surface of the enamel tray you'll use.

Acetic Acid proportions:

28% (Photo): use 1½ ounces of 28% solution to each 32 ounces of water.
99% (Glacial): add 3 parts of 99% solution to 8 parts of water to make a 28% solution, and then dilute as given for 28%.

Important warning:

Be especially careful that you do not get 99% glacial acetic on your skin as it causes severe burn. Should this happen, immediately wash with water.

The main reason you'd buy 99% acetic acid would be to save darkroom space and to save money (packaging and shipping charges of acetic acid are a major part of the cost because of volume and weight and the fact that it must be shipped in sturdy glass bottles).

Use of acetic acid is important in the darkroom when you need to turn out a number of prints exactly alike. It stops the development and stalemates the progress of the prints until you take the last of the prints from the developer. Then, with undivided attention, you can give the individual prints proper immersion in the hypo, since the importance of *proper* fixation cannot be understated.

It is not necessary to count the number of prints you put through your tray of acetic-acid working solution, since the life of the solution depends upon too many variables to allow for a "formula" approach to the question of when to change the short stop. The time and care with which you drain the developer from your print before immersion in the acetic acid will vary with the individual worker—as well as with the time of night. Double-weight prints carry more developer into the acetic tray than single-weight prints. Cold acetic-acid working solution will take longer to stop the action of the developer.

You can best determine that your acetic solution is working well by looking and listening for the effervescent action, the bubbles coming through the back of the print. Advisably, you place the print into the acetic tray face down so that you can push the print at numerous points with your tongs. Should the bubbles fail to appear after twenty or thirty seconds you can assume that your solution is too weak to start with or somewhat exhausted. If exhaustion is the fault, you can revitalize the working solution by adding acetic acid. With the light on, check that the acetic solution isn't yellow like a tray of old, exhausted developer: if it is, adding acetic acid is sending good money after bad—the only thing to do is dump the tray and start with a fresh short stop bath.

Proper Fixing

Up to this point the hypo part of the photographic process has been taken pretty much for granted: it is the tank or tray where we automatically place the film or prints after development. If we are quick to realize that the fixing step isn't magic and that there are do's and don'ts, we'll soon be producing more permanent negatives and prints. Properly fixed prints wash better, gloss better, curl less, and tone more

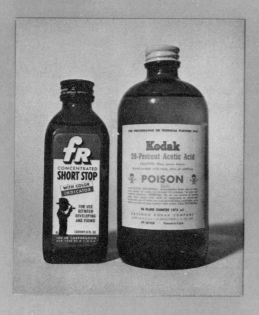

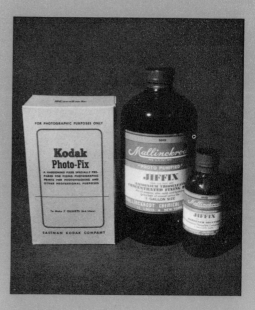

Acetic acid is used between developer and fixer. It stops the action of developer, neutralizing the alkalis so that hypo can do job more effectively.

Hypos are available in many forms, from few-ounce envelope to 100-pound bag. Above, Photo-Fix is for prints; Jiffix is one-minute hypo for negs.

evenly. To obtain these benefits you will have to show the same loving care to the print during fixing and washing that you gave it during the exposure and development.

The desired total time in the hypo should be twice the "clearing" time. In the case of prints it is not easy to determine this fixing time with the print itself, so take a piece of unexposed paper (which has been soaked in water to soften the emulsion as if it had undergone development) and insert it halfway into your hypo bath. The top portion will remain yellowish and the part in the hypo will become clear. Note the time it takes to clear, and double it to determine the *fixing time*. Fixing time includes hardening as well as clearing.

Rapid fixers (ammonium thiosulfate) usually "clear" the film in about half a minute while the regular fixers (sodium thiosulfate) will require about three minutes for "clearing." The rapid fixer should be quite satisfactory for reuse as long as the total fixing time of the used solution is not more than five times the total fixing time when fresh. The regular-speed fixer works well up to a point twice the fixing time of fresh starting solution. This difference is in the capacity of the rapid fixer to

hold more silver. It is not a crime to use either type of hypo beyond these points, but in so doing you run the risk of having the silver that's in suspension redeposited onto your prints. Think back to this discussion when you first notice unexplainable brown and yellow stains on your prints.

All of this points to the recommended use of the rapid fixers, or the modern single-powder fixers containing ammonium thiosulfate. A word of caution: their rapid action can go beyond the fixing time and turn to slight bleaching. (If you doubt this, leave a print in a fresh solution of rapid fixer for twelve hours!) If possible, determine your normal rate of printing so that you can take a print out of the hypo and place it in the circulating wash water every second or third print, depending on how fast you work. In case you have developed half a dozen prints together, the most important thing to do is agitate the prints in the hypo as carefully as if it were film just starting the developing cycle. Give them an occasional shuffle, several times during the fixing period. The use of a tray considerably larger than the prints—space permitting—will be of great value here. The most rapid fixer in the world doesn't have a chance to act when the prints are stacked in solu-

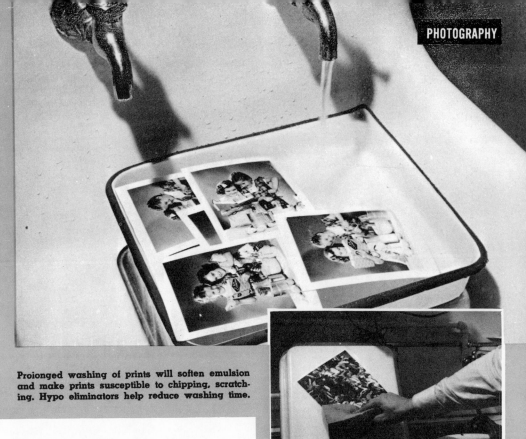

Prolonged washing of prints will soften emulsion and make prints susceptible to chipping, scratching. Hypo eliminators help reduce washing time.

Inset above shows matte print being wiped off with a sponge to remove excess moisture after washing, before placing print in blotter book, blotter roll.

tion in one big clump. True, the edges will fix, but hardly the center areas. Stains on the prints are another indication of poor circulation of prints in the hypo—so there's a second explanation of stains after you've decided that you are *not* using exhausted hypo.

Either regular or rapid hypo remains good until used. It does not oxidize, in the sense that a tray of developer turns deep brown. However, stored in open trays the hypo is subject to the evaporation of both its water and acetic acid content. Bottle the hypo if weeks go by between each printing session. Otherwise, jack it up with water and acetic acid to bring the volume to the point where it was when first mixed.

Washing Prints

Print washing is often thought of as a vague amount of time devoted to removing the hypo while you have a sandwich and a cup of coffee or clean up the darkroom a bit. But it is far more important than you may realize. Again, as in film and print developing, we come to that photographically all-important word "agitation." Don't leave your prints in the wash water for extra hours as a substitute for hand agitation. This can only cause the emulsion

eventually to swell and chip. When selecting trays for washing in the home darkroom, always obtain at least the next size larger than the prints to be washed. This is to permit better circulation of the wash water. And a plastic tray syphon is a very useful gadget to own.

Cold water in the northern regions of the United States often runs below 40 degrees in the winter and is of little help in washing away the hypo, no matter how long you wash. Blend some warm water with this to bring it up to 65 degrees, and not over 75 degrees. There are several hypo eliminators available but these are mainly time-savers, and thorough washing can do the same work. •

Print Finishing

Quality prints are the mark of a fine photographic workman. Here is how you can achieve top results.

IT is important that your print be properly hardened and thoroughly washed before you start it on any drying process, whether glossy or matte finish. Make certain that there is no dirt or sediment from the wash water clinging to the surface of the print.

Glossy prints obtain their gloss in the drying process, which in effect is a glazing of the paper's enameled surface. The advantage of a true glossy print is that a maximum amount of the print detail is re-tained. For a visual comparison make two identical prints on glossy paper and dry one with a gloss (by ferrotyping) and the second without a gloss. For one thing, you will see that the blacks appear blacker in the ferrotyped print, and that this print has more over-all sparkle and contrast.

Place the print in a tray of water containing a wetting agent or print conditioner (after print washing is complete). Two well known examples of these are Ansco Flexogloss and Pako's Pakosol, both of

Steady, even roller pressure is essential to assure good contact for high gloss prints, as at left. For the initial few rolls on a print it is necessary and important to use blotters to pick up moisture.

To minimize the curl in matte or glossy prints, place them face to face (emulsion to emulsion) in pairs and put them under a pile of heavy books. If your drying methods produce prints that have a curl, and you can't remedy this with Flexogloss, it might be of value to obtain a screw-type print-flattening press for regular use.

p the print make better contact ferrotyping surface for a better tend to make the prints less curly ed. Kodak's universal wetting to-Flo, which you use for nega- re hanging them to dry can also for photographic prints. More ossy prints will result, ones which ss subject to cracks in the emul-

tion to various sizes of electric eated dryers, there are two basic

types of ferrotype plates, or "tins," for use in a darkroom arrangement that has a small or occasional output: the black enamel ferrotype plate and the chromium-finish plate. Size for size, the black enamel tins cost about half as much as the chrome tins, thereby providing more glossy drying surface per dollar—if that interests you. Black tins cannot be heated and consequently require a longer time to deliver a glossy print. They require considerable care in handling and an occasional "waxing" with a blend

Before placing your matte or semi-matte print into a blotter roll, make sure it has been thoroughly washed. Sponge off excess moisture, place print so emulsion faces outside curve of blotter.

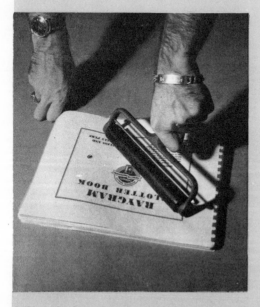

In blotter book, emulsion faces wax-paper separator sheet, so never place book near heat. Print roller helps blotter absorb moisture from prints. It's good idea to transfer prints in book while drying.

of paraffin and carbon tetrachloride. There are still oldtime professional shops around the country who swear by the black enamel tins, but the trend is to the chrome-on-brass finish. This latter may be heated if necessary to speed up the drying, and requires no waxing and little more attention than an occasional Bon Ami cleansing. Sponge off the tins between each print load, and wipe with a dry cloth before using to insure a dust-free condition.

The important thing in all glossy-print drying is that the print is firmly rolled onto the drying surface and that most of the water is pressured out of the backing of the print. Good contact will assure a good gloss. Most rotary dryers have mechanisms built in to apply roller pressure for extracting moisture from the print; however, in using flat and nearly flat ferrotype plates, with or without heat, it is most important that you proceed as follows:

1. Wet the surface of the plate before placing the wet print on it. The exception is when you apply a print to an already hot ferrotype plate, and in this case you must work very rapidly to squeegee out the water (that is, roll it out under pressure)· otherwise the print will not adhere to the plate.

2. Place a blotter or piece of Scott towel over the back of the print, and roll over it with a print roller with moderate pressure to assure good contact for a high gloss.

3. Remove the blotter and check the back of the print with your fingertips for air spaces where the print hasn't made contact, and for pieces of dirt between the print and surface of the ferrotype plate. If not removed, dirt will cause pit marks on the surface of the print.

4. When it appears that there are no air spaces or dirt, run the print roller over the print again, this time directly on the back of the print and without the blotter.

5. Regular tins require patience from this point on as there is little you can do but wait for the air to dry the prints. (Heated flat dryers require the weight of a number of dry blotters to hold the edges of the print flat while the center area is still drying. Some heated dryers come equipped with a canvas cover which is stretched into place to hold the print flat for the entire drying process. Home-model rotary dryers have a built-in squeegee and thus eliminate the rolling and blotting and re-rolling steps.)

Should you find the curl of a single-weight glossy print bothersome, the following remedies are suggested:

1. Weight the print as soon as it comes

off the tin. If there are a number of prints, place some of them face to face so that the curl of one print paper opposes the curl of the facing print. (Photographic paper is made on huge rolls, much in the manner of news print, and it has to age properly on rolls before it is cut into sheets and placed on the market—this accounts for the curl usually present.)

2. Moisten the back of the print with a damp sponge and flex it in a direction opposite to the curl. Then place it under a blotter weight to flatten.

3. If your single-weight prints still curl too much and you need the glossy finish, try using double-weight glossy stock. The heavier paper tends to offset the curl and the pull of the emulsion.

Poor quality in the glossy finish of a print will detract from the craftsmanship that has gone into making the print up to the point of drying. It would be wise to understand the faults that can occur in ferrotyping so that they can be eliminated.

Glossy prints that continue to stick to the ferrotype surface after they are dry are usually the result of softness of the gelatin due to improper fixing (exhausted hypo, insufficient fixing). To remove prints from flat (non-electric) tins, soak the tin together with the print in lukewarm water until the print slides free, then re-harden it in a fresh fixing bath. Insufficient washing and dirty tins can also cause sticking.

Air bells that have been trapped under the surface of a print form dull circular or oval marks. This lack of print-to-tin contact calls for more care in squeegeeing the print plus the use of a wetting agent in the final water dip.

Excessive heat will cause "oyster shell" marks on the surface of the print as a result of too fast a drying process. Extreme results will be cracks in the emulsion. To prevent this, reduce the heat (on an electric dryer), use a print flattening solution, and place moisture-absorbing blotters against the backs of prints on flat tins. This type of flaw occurs chiefly in winter, and is traceable to low humidity.

Prints that dry unevenly at the edges and not at the center can be improved by presoaking in a print-flattening solution before heat drying. Double-weight prints are most susceptible to this uneven drying.

Dull finish, or insufficient gloss, can be caused by pulling the print from the ferrotype surface before the gelatin has completely dried. A black enamel tin that has not been waxed will give a dull finish. Excessive hardening will cause small unglazed pit marks. Cold tap water in the winter

months is often too cold to do a proper print washing job and a warmer wash should be used, as near to 65 to 70 degrees as possible. Hot water can be used on a properly hardened print in an emergency but is not recommended. If water temperature can't be regulated, the print should be hand washed by holding under a faucet and allowing water to run from corner to corner, rotating constantly.

Color, or tone, changes can result from excessive heat in drying. Some of these changes are the result of too strong or prolonged fixing or insufficient hypo elimination because of incomplete washing. Other changes are inherent in the paper and, if heat drying is to be used, should be learned as a part of the printing process.

Matte Prints

Matte is the general term for all prints that are not dried glossy (ferrotyped). The range of matte surface is from smooth finish to coarse, textured finish. Never attempt to dry a matte paper glossy, or the emulsion will come off on the plate. *Semi-matte* surface has a luster that resembles glossy; *semi-gloss* is a non-ferrotyping glossy surface.

After proper hardening and thorough washing (which should be thought of as the first steps in any drying process, even though they are on the wet side), drain all excess water from your matte prints and with light roller pressure, or by using a wad of long-fiber cotton or a viscose sponge, remove as much remaining moisture as possible. Place the prints between lintless blotters with a slight weight on top. Drying can be accelerated by moving prints to a second set of weighted blotters after about a half hour.

If you use one of the commercially prepared blotter books, be sure that you don't try to speed things up by heating the book, since this will cause the waxed separator pages to adhere to the prints. If you use a blotter roll, secure it so that there will be pressure on the prints. Electric dryers can be used to dry matte prints by placing the picture (emulsion) side against the canvas curtain, or away from the heated tin with several changes of weighted blotters.

A number of darkroom workers who use Varigam as a means of reducing paper inventory (as well as because they like it) go a step further and use "T" surface, which is double-weight glossy paper for both glossy and matte prints. Dried with the emulsion side away from the ferrotyping surface, "T" dries just about the same as

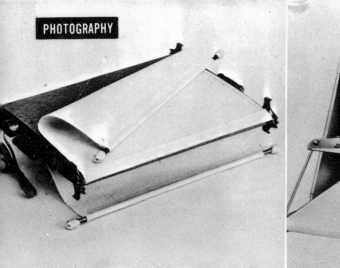
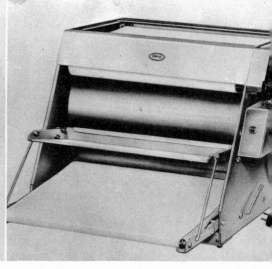

Left, inexpensive electric dryer handles prints on both sides and is useful when you have just a few prints to dry. Use roller or squeegee for good contact. Home-model continuous belt dryer handles up to 50 single-weight glossies per hour, has adjustable speed, heat controls for various prints.

the semi-matte papers in the Varigam and Velour Black lines. There is the further advantage of being able to convert any of these exhibition mattes into a reproduction glossy merely by re-wetting and ferrotyping it.

Spotting Can Make a Print

Aside from a poor glossy finish or outright chemical stains on the face of the print, there is nothing as distracting in a good print as the need for spotting—the elimination of scratches, pinholes, dust marks. Before describing the procedure for "spotting" out these defects, it would be well to take up a method of eliminating the need for spotting: Simply clean your negative with a camel's hair brush *after* placing it in the negative carrier. A few seconds spent on this will save minutes after the print has been processed and dried. And where more than one print is to be made from the negative, the dust-spotting process can be a real time problem.

Needless to say, glassless carriers offer fewer dust-holding surfaces; glass carriers should be considered only in association with an autofocus enlarger. Check the condensers of your enlarger frequently for dust. Vacuum the darkroom every once in a while to collect the existing dust before it settles on the negative you are printing.

Negatives that hold dust to their surface and which don't respond to the touch of camel's hair brush can be cleaned with long-fiber cotton and carbon tetrachloride. Apply the moistened cotton with long, even strokes, all in the same direction across the negative.

Spotting colors come in 3-inch panels and in three main colors: white, black, and sepia. The addition of the white to either black or sepia will cover the whole range of spotting chores which will come up. Buy a good camel's hair brush with a tip at least as fine as the point on a sharpened pencil. Dampen the tip of the brush and touch it to the spotting color. For extremely fine spots a better point can be obtained on the brush by twisting the tip of it slightly after it has been moistened. Blacks are the easiest print areas to work on as there is hardly any matching to do. Start with blacks to get the feel of the brush and the reaction of the print surface to accepting the color. Generally the black color is added to the white on the spotting panel; therefore you'll need a new set of spotting colors each time the white panel has been blended down beyond most of the useful gray tones.

Grays and the middle tones through white are a little more exacting, and an extra glossy print is always handy as a test patch for the color blend before applying color to the print that needs it. If you

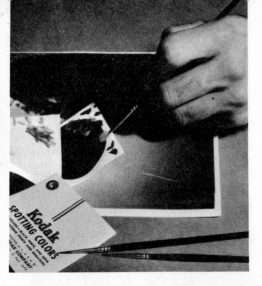
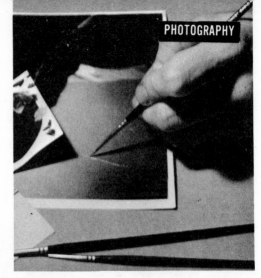

Spotting colors come in white, black and sepia. The tip of a moistened brush is used to blend colors as required. Sable or camel's-hair brushes are used to apply spotting color. It will be helpful to have two or three with different tips on hand. Color is removed with piece of damp cotton.

apply the wrong shade, one that is a poor match with the tone on the print, merely wipe it away with a slightly damp piece of cotton.

The idea is to cover the spot with just enough color to make it match. Large areas of spotting are noticeable. It is suggested that you add a bit of mucilage to the spotting color for use on glossy prints, since this will give the spotted dots a shine similar to the gloss of the print. Experience will show you that often a dot or two of black or gray will suffice to break up a dust spot on a print, and this will require less time than trying to fill in the spot completely. Make pinpoint dots similar to the screen pattern in the daily newspaper's photoengraving: you'll work faster. Spotting colors will wash off, so keep that in mind if for any reason you intend to rewash and dry a spotted print.

Laquering Prints for Display

Perhaps you have examined one of your more beautiful prints in the wash water and sighed to yourself: "If it only would look that good when it dried!" What you are complaining about, of course, is the behavior of all matte and textured papers and many of the semi-mattes. Blotter drying or minimum heat drying makes most prints appear dark, as though they'd be just about right if they'd had about 10% less exposure.

It would be perfectly logical to compensate so the prints would seem "10% light" when viewed in the hypo and "right" when dried. However, this compensating process overlooks the question of *brilliance.* (And turning to a glossy paper eliminates the use of textures that can be very effective under many display conditions.)

While this seems quite a perplexing situation, it is really easy to resolve with a practice, little used these days, of surfacing the prints with a clear, colorless lacquer. This restores the "shine" into the blacks—not unlike glossy paper and yet permitting the texture to show through. Then there is no need for a compensating process of using a double standard in print judgment, one for the hypo and another for the dried print. Also, spotting marks are covered over by the lacquer and are practically unnoticed. But be certain to select a colorless, shiny lacquer—a dull lacquer brings you no place.

Application of lacquer can be performed right on the print after it has been drymounted (see the following chapter). Mask off the mounting mask itself so that no lacquer is sprayed on it. Use a small artist's fixative atomizer to apply the lacquer. Then immediately turn the mount over so that the print dries face down, to prevent the wet lacquer from collecting dust that is in the air. To do this, support edges of the mount on a 2x2 board. •

Simon Nathan

Mounting the Print

**Good prints are meant to be seen, not to be stored away from view.
Display them in albums and on photo mounts for effective presentation.**

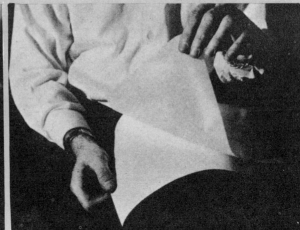

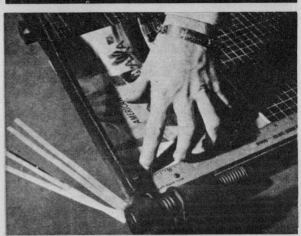

Tacking iron is touched to the center of the dry-mounting tissue on the back of the print. On prints 8x10 or larger, a straight line stroke is made.

Top right, test of assembly is that tissue does not pull away from print. This is important so that both tissue and print can be trimmed to same size.

When trimming the print it is important to extend the fingers of the hand over a large area of the print to make sure it is perfectly flat prior to cutting.

SOMEWHERE along the line you'll be producing contact prints and enlargements of the highest quality, ones which deserve more recognition than storage in an old desk drawer. Photo albums and wall displays are two major presentations requiring proper mounting of your prints. Small prints up to 2¼x4¼ can be mounted with rubber cement, but sizes beyond this point are more easily handled with easy-to-use dry-mounting tissue.

Dry-mounting tissue is simply a sheet of thermoplastic paper which forms a bond between the print and the album page (or photo mount) when heated. It is odorless, not sticky to handle, and certainly will not discolor the print. It permits accurate placing of the print before the final "tie-down," and prints so mounted may be

removed when necessary through the re-application of heat. Dry-mounting tissue is available in just about every standard contact and enlarging paper size. You can buy it in an envelope of only ten sheets, or in a box of 100 sheets, measuring up to 16x20 inches, and beyond this size in roll form. For album use with varied print sizes it is advisable to buy the largest size you'll use and then cut smaller sizes from a whole sheet.

Generally, a device known as a dry-mounting press (see photos) is used to apply the heat to the print-and-tissue sandwich for the final bond to the display surface. Presses come in sizes as small as 8x10 and as large as 16x20, and have thermostats to control different heat requirements (as for double- and single-

With a piece of thin cardboard or kraft paper on print, touch the tacking iron to the assembly to place it in the exact position for mounting.

When a salon mount is used, the print, with the tissues tacked to the back, is slipped into the mount and then tacked into permanent position.

weight papers). Heat is applied over the whole area of the print, with enough pressure to assure an even bond. Buy a dry-mounting press only as large as you really need; it will prove costly to heat a 16x20 platen to mount several 5x7 prints.

You actually don't need a dry-mounting press to take advantage of this method of mounting your prints. The home automatic electric iron is quite satisfactory. Or slightly better would be one of the hand model dry-mounting irons on the market, which are rectangle-shaped rather than triangular like the iron around the house. This hand dry-mounting iron is set thermostatically for the heat required by the two major brands of dry-mounting tissue. Also it will be found useful for artistically mounting small prints directly to the wallboard in your home—a rather difficult feat to perform with a dry-mounting press.

A *tacking iron* is a necessary accessory with a dry-mounting press. Use the edge of the iron to "tack" the dry-mounting tissue to the back of the print: do this before final trimming of the prints so that the tissue does not extend beyond the area of the print. No pressure should be applied with the tacking iron. One small spot of contact is sufficient for snapshot-sized prints. An 8x10 print is best tacked with three or four such "spot welds" of the tissue to the back of the print (toward the inside, not on the outer edges of the print). Larger prints require careful tacking so that the tissue is flat over the whole back of the

print, and "valleys" and air spaces will not be created. When using a household electric iron, tacking is done with the toe of the iron.

It may save you money and grief to know that Kodacolor prints should not be mounted by any process requiring the use of heat, as the dyes are certain to be affected. Kodachrome prints can be mounted with Eastman Thermount tissue if you will go to the slight extra effort of roughing up the glossy back side with a bit of fine sandpaper. Kodak's Resisto enlarging paper doesn't seem to work with anybody's dry-mounting tissue but it is unlikely that the average print-maker would be using this paper for display prints.

After checking for dirt and other extraneous matter, tack the dry-mounting tissue to the back of the print. Trim the print with the dry-mounting tissue attached, making sure to press the print out flat for the trimming operation (otherwise the mounted print will show an excess of tissue). After placing the print-and-tissue combination on the album page or salon mount, cover the surface of the print with a piece of heavy kraft paper or very light, thin cardboard. Place about one-third of the print area under the platen of the dry-mounting press. If you are using a home iron or hand dry-mounting iron, apply heat to just enough print area to hold it in place for inspection. What you need to know at this point, and before applying heat to the whole print, is that the print is exactly

A cardboard insert is placed into the opening in the die-cut salon mount to take up difference in depth, so as to transfer heat on print evenly.

The whole "sandwich" of print, tissue, cardboard and mount is placed in the dry-mounting press and the "heat door" of the press is then lowered.

where you want it, that it lines up with the edges of the page or mount, and that it hasn't shifted in the process of placing the three-layer sandwich into the press.

The length of time and the amount of heat for completing the bond are directly related to each other. The amount of heat required to do a satisfactory dry-mounting job is determined by: 1) thickness of the printing stock (single weight, double weight), 2) brand of tissue used (Fotoflat, Eastman Thermount, Eastman Dry Mounting Tissue), 3) weight of surface on which print is to be mounted (examples varying from lightweight album page to the heavy board of a salon mount), and 4) nature of surface to which you want the tissue to adhere. For example, the time on the Seal dry-mounting press with Fotoflat tissue will be around 3 seconds for a single-weight print with operating temperature set at 225 degrees. The Seal press has a flashing red light for counting the seconds, and a firm sponge-rubber bed which prevents the seam that often appears when a print is only partially mounted and then checked for position before total heat.

As soon as you remove your mounted print from the press, or have completed the heating with a hand iron, place it on a flat surface to cool, under a moderate weight to assure complete contact. Examine the print for air spaces which appear at points where the dry-mounting tissue hasn't made a bond. Check that the print edges are flush to the surface of the mount.

Mechanically, the dry-mounting process is fairly routine. However, there are several important factors to consider even before making the display print. The first is to determine what size print will be "right" for a specific display point; in fancier words, the viewing distance should determine the size of the print. Pictures so small that you have to cross the room to examine their content are of little value and perhaps better belong in an album rather than on a wall. The reverse is true: don't expect a 16x20 print to be appreciated in a narrow 4-foot hall.

Outside dimensions of 16x20 inches are just about standard the world over wherever pictures are exhibited. Prints themselves may run as small as 8x10, while mounted on a 16x20 board. Generally, prints are 14x17 or 11x14 inches, either horizontal or vertical, and are mounted as shown. Exceptions are made by placing a print off center when it adds to the effectiveness of the composition. No rule can be written for this and it will depend pretty much on the content of the photograph and how it has been cropped.

If you don't have enough wall space for 16x20 mounts and would like to get more prints into view, a good mounting and display technique is the submount. Mount your print on standard photographic mounting board (available in camera stores and art supply houses) and allow ¼ inch of board to show beyond the edge of the print. ●

PICNIC SET JUNIOR

By David X. Manners

*Safe and comfortable, this pint-sized picnic table can
be built in three hours for six dollars.*

GIVE THE YOUNGSTERS a picnic
table of their own, and tailor it to
fit their size. They'll find it more comfortable to eat at than a grownup table,
and more fun. Betweentimes, they can
use it as a play table, indoors or out.
Attached benches can't get knocked
over, are safer.

You can easily build the table with
its attached benches using hand tools
only. Unit is made of redwood or pine.

For the project buy four 12-foot
lengths of 1x4 and one 7-foot length of
5/4x2. Cut two of the 12-foot lengths
into 3-foot pieces. Cut two more 3-foot
pieces off the next 12-footer. These ten
pieces will make the top and seats. Out
of what remains of the cut 12-footer,
you can get one 43-inch length for a
seat-supporting crosspiece and have
plenty left over for making two 1x2
braces, each 14¾ inches long. Bevel
the ends of the braces on their flat side
at a 45-degree angle.

GETTING THE YOUNGSTERS OFF ON THEIR OWN at cookouts will mean more fun for
them and more relaxation for you. Betweentimes, handy unit can be used as play table.

ENDS OF LEGS are cut at 60° angle. If you own a power saw, set it for this angle.

DRILL LEG HOLES simultaneously on drill press or, holding plumb, with hand drill.

FOR HANDSAW CUT on legs, approximate 60° angle marking deep side 1⅞ inches in.

CUT ENDS of crosspieces which support seats at 45° angle, square off ends ¾ in.

Out of the remaining 12-footer, you can cut the four legs needed and a second seat-supporting crosspiece. Both ends of each leg are cut at a 60-degree angle. If you have a table or radial saw, merely set the gauges for that cut. For handsawing, draw the line of cut by connecting a point on one side of the board with a point 1⅞ inches farther along on the other side. Legs measure 22 inches on a side, but because of the angle cut, their overall length is approximately 24 inches.

Ends of both 43-inch crosspieces are cut at a 45-degree angle. Make both cuts angle inward. The short side that results will measure 36 inches. Square off the pointed ends ¾ inch back. The long side will then measure 41½ inches.

Use a ¼-inch bit for all hole drilling. Measure ½ inch from the end of one of the legs and draw a line paralleling the end. This line will measure 4 inches in length. Mark holes for drilling at points 1 inch from each end of the line. These holes will be two inches apart. Make a pair of similar holes, 11 inches away, on a line paralleling the first line.

All legs are drilled similarly. For greatest accuracy, however, measure and drill each leg separately.

One of the best finishes for the picnic table is Rez, a color-toned, penetrating wood sealer. It is available in a variety of finishes including redwood and cedar. It is best applied to the table parts before assembly, for then you can cover all surfaces completely. Assemble with $\frac{3}{16}$-inch machine screws, nuts and washers. Get them cadmium-plated and they'll never rust and stain the wood. Use 2-inch long machine screws in fastening legs, 3-inch screws elsewhere. •

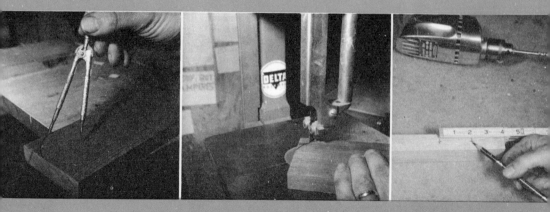

ROUND OFF table and seat corners as shown. Set compass or scriber at a 1¾-inch radius to mark line of corner and cut on jig saw or band saw. Sand all edges with fine-grit paper. Drill holes in side of table cleats two and four inches in from each end as shown.

DRAWING below exploded view of the table's construction. Lifted top allows clear view of placement of cleats as well as bench and leg detail. Note lighter weight wood used.

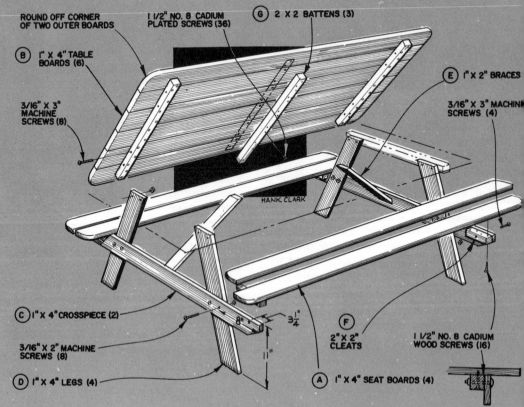

ROUND OFF CORNER OF TWO OUTER BOARDS

1 1/2" NO. 8 CADIUM PLATED SCREWS (36)

G   2 X 2 BATTENS (3)

B   1" X 4" TABLE BOARDS (6)

E   1" X 2" BRACES

3/16" X 3" MACHINE SCREWS (8)

3/16" X 3" MACHINE SCREWS (4)

HANK CLARK

C   1" X 4" CROSSPIECE (2)

3/16" X 2" MACHINE SCREWS (8)

D   1" X 4" LEGS (4)

F   2" X 2" CLEATS

1 1/2" NO. 8 CADIUM WOOD SCREWS (16)

A   1" X 4" SEAT BOARDS (4)

3¼"

8"

11"

ATTACH CLEATS to seats and table top by setting two 1½-in. cadmium-plated wood screws through cleats into board bottoms.

SAND ALL SURFACES to prepare for finish, then apply liberal coating of Rez, a color-toned penetrating sealer, before assembly.

SCREWING BRACES to table, upper right, attach slightly off center to miss middle crack between boards making up table top.

FOR OUTDOOR USE, right, cadmium-plated machine screws should be used to prevent rust. Place nuts and washers toward inside.

PLAN FOR CUTTING lumber, below, assures full use of material with minimum of waste.

ALL PARTS FROM 1" X 4" X 12 FT. STOCK (4 LENGTHS)

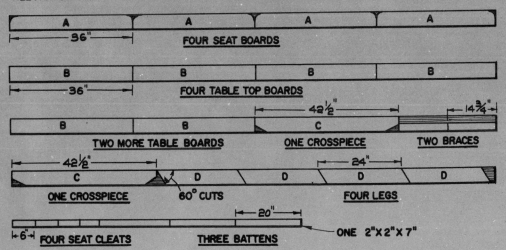

A	A	A	A

├─ 36" ─┤ **FOUR SEAT BOARDS**

B	B	B	B

├─ 36" ─┤ **FOUR TABLE TOP BOARDS**

├──── 42½" ────┤   ├─ 14¾" ─┤

B	B	C	TWO BRACES

TWO MORE TABLE BOARDS   **ONE CROSSPIECE**

├──── 42½" ────┤   ├── 24" ──┤

C	D	D	D	D

ONE CROSSPIECE   **60° CUTS**   **FOUR LEGS**

├── 20" ──┤

FOUR SEAT CLEATS   **THREE BATTENS**   ONE 2" X 2" X 7"

├6"┤

Cabinet holds all odds and ends of silver-ware and bottles, serves as table, folds up neatly for stowage in the trunk of the car.

Portable Picnic Cabinet

PICNICS are more fun for everybody if they can be enjoyed in comfort. Instead of trying to eat off uneven ground, use this portable cabinet. It not only provides a smooth surface, but it also discourages ground insects from joining in the feast.

Secret of this cabinet is that the door panels spread out to form legs. The entire unit folds up neatly and can be stowed in the trunk of the car.

It can be constructed with simple hand tools since no difficult cuts or joints are required. First cut all parts to size and begin by assembling sides and top. Glue and nail plywood dividers into position and install hinged legs and table leaves. Paint the cabinet in bright gay colors using a semi-gloss enamel. Catches and handle are installed after painting. •

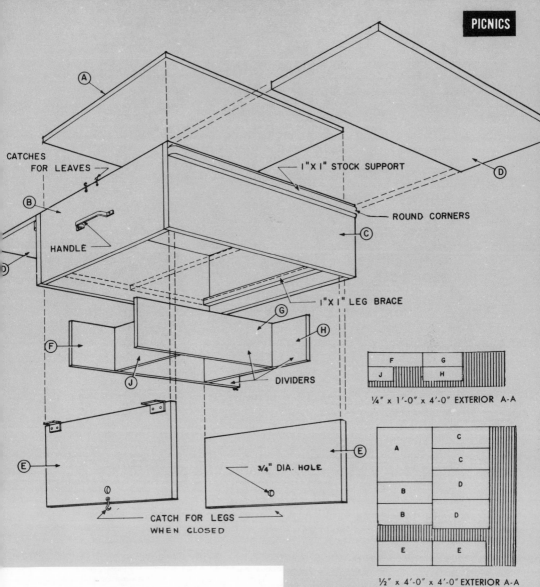

CATCHES FOR LEAVES

HANDLE

(A)

(B)

(C)

(D)

1"X 1" STOCK SUPPORT

ROUND CORNERS

1"X 1" LEG BRACE

(F) (G) (H) (J)

DIVIDERS

(E)

3/4" DIA. HOLE

CATCH FOR LEGS
WHEN CLOSED

| F | | G | |
| J | | H | |

1/4" x 1'-0" x 4'-0" EXTERIOR A-A

A		C	
		C	
B		D	
B		D	
E		E	

1/2" x 4'-0" x 4'-0" EXTERIOR A-A

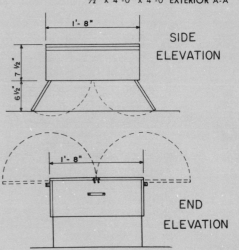

1'- 8"

7 1/2"

6 1/2"

SIDE ELEVATION

1'- 8"

END ELEVATION

PARTS SCHEDULE

CODE	NO. REQ'D	SIZE	PART IDENTIFICATION
A	1	19"x19"	Top
B	2	7½"x19"	Side
C	2	7½"x20"	Side
D	2	9-15/16"x20"	Top Door
E	2	8⅝"x19"	Bottom Door
F	1	5"x19"	Divider
G	1	5"x14"	Divider
H	1	5"x14"	Divider
J	1	5"x9"	Divider
	5 Ea.	—	Catches and Pins
	1 Ea.	—	Metal Handle
	7 Lin. Ft.	1"x1"	Leaf and Leg Supports
	8 Ea.	—	Hinges

Miscellaneous—4d Finish Nails (Galvanized)
Waterproof Glue

2199

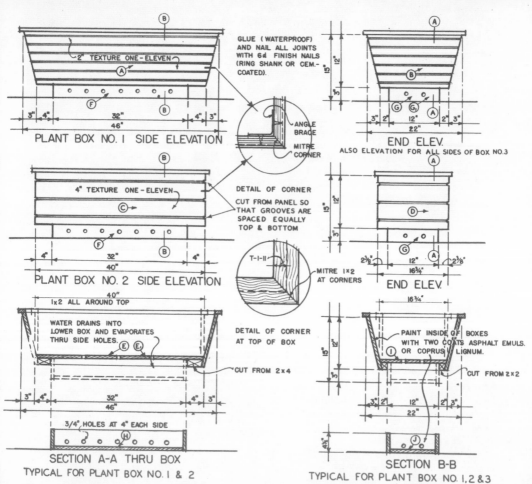

GLUE (WATERPROOF) AND NAIL ALL JOINTS WITH 6d FINISH NAILS (RING SHANK OR CEM.-COATED).

2" TEXTURE ONE-ELEVEN

PLANT BOX NO. I SIDE ELEVATION

3" 4" 32" 4" 3"
46"

ANGLE BRACE
MITRE CORNER

DETAIL OF CORNER

CUT FROM PANEL SO THAT GROOVES ARE SPACED EQUALLY TOP & BOTTOM

4" TEXTURE ONE-ELEVEN

PLANT BOX NO. 2 SIDE ELEVATION

4" 32" 4"
40"

END ELEV.
ALSO ELEVATION FOR ALL SIDES OF BOX NO.3

12"
15"
3"
3" 2" 12" 2" 3"
22"

T-1-11
MITRE 1 x 2 AT CORNERS

DETAIL OF CORNER AT TOP OF BOX

END ELEV.

12"
15"
3"
2⅜" 12" 2⅜"
16¾"

40"
1x2 ALL AROUND TOP

WATER DRAINS INTO LOWER BOX AND EVAPORATES THRU SIDE HOLES.

CUT FROM 2 x 4

3" 4" 32" 4" 3"
46"

3/4" HOLES AT 4" EACH SIDE

SECTION A-A THRU BOX
TYPICAL FOR PLANT BOX NO. I & 2

16¾"

PAINT INSIDE OF BOXES WITH TWO COATS ASPHALT EMULS. OR COPRUS W LIGNUM.

CUT FROM 2 x 2

12"
15"
3"
3" 2" 12" 2" 3"
22"

4½"

SECTION B-B
TYPICAL FOR PLANT BOX NO. 1, 2 & 3

plant boxes

These three modular designs will add beauty to your garden

THE modern panel siding material used for these modular plant boxes achieves a smart surface design with little effort.

As illustrated, the three designs can be mingled, or you may arrange similar boxes in a pattern that complements or contrasts with your setting.

Cut bottom panel to size for box you build. Use only Exterior type plywood made with 100% waterproof glue. Drill drain holes.

Cut Texture One-Eleven plywood sides and ends to size and miter at corners. Check for perfect fit to prevent leaks be-fore assembling. This will save much time.

Cut 2x2 and 2x4-inch bottom frame to size. If building designs 1 or 3, bevel sides, framing and bottom panel to conform to slope.

Nail and glue framing to bottom, then nail sides to frame. Glue mitered corners and clamp tightly together inside with angle braces and short screws.

Miter 1x2-inch top frame, nail in place and paint inside as recommended.

Cut and drill parts for drainage boxes as required, assemble with waterproof glue and nails and finish completely. ●

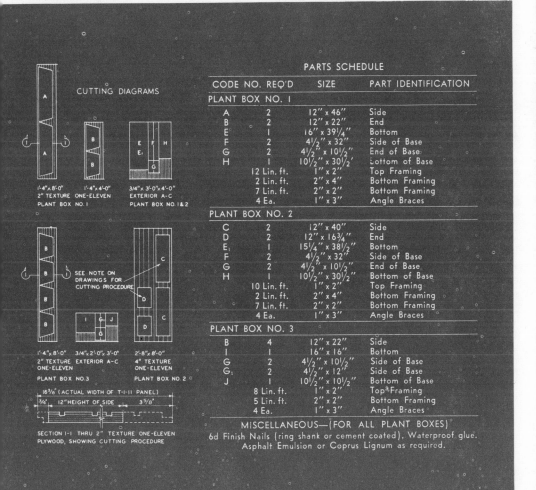

CUTTING DIAGRAMS

1'-4" x 8'-0"
2" TEXTURE ONE-ELEVEN
PLANT BOX NO. 1

1'-4" x 4'-0"

3/4" x 3'-0" x 4'-0"
EXTERIOR A-C
PLANT BOX NO. 1 & 2

SEE NOTE ON DRAWINGS FOR CUTTING PROCEDURE

1'-4" x 8'-0"
2" TEXTURE
ONE-ELEVEN
PLANT BOX NO. 3

3/4" x 2'-0" x 3'-0"
EXTERIOR A-C

2'-8" x 8'-0"
4" TEXTURE
ONE-ELEVEN
PLANT BOX NO. 2

16 3/8" (ACTUAL WIDTH OF T-I-II PANEL)

3/4" | 12" HEIGHT OF SIDE | 3 5/8"

SECTION 1-1 THRU 2" TEXTURE ONE-ELEVEN PLYWOOD, SHOWING CUTTING PROCEDURE

PARTS SCHEDULE

CODE NO.	REQ'D	SIZE	PART IDENTIFICATION
PLANT BOX NO. 1			
A	2	12" x 46"	Side
B	2	12" x 22"	End
E	1	16" x 39¼"	Bottom
F	2	4½" x 32"	Side of Base
G	2	4½" x 10½"	End of Base
H	1	10½" x 30½'	Bottom of Base
	12 Lin. ft.	1" x 2"	Top Framing
	2 Lin. ft.	2" x 4"	Bottom Framing
	7 Lin. ft.	2" x 2"	Bottom Framing
	4 Ea.	1" x 3"	Angle Braces
PLANT BOX NO. 2			
C	2	12" x 40"	Side
D	2	12" x 16¾"	End
E₁	1	15¼" x 38½"	Bottom
F	2	4½" x 32"	Side of Base
G	2	4½" x 10½"	End of Base
H	1	10½" x 30½"	Bottom of Base
	10 Lin. ft.	1" x 2"	Top Framing
	2 Lin. ft.	2" x 4"	Bottom Framing
	7 Lin. ft.	2" x 2"	Bottom Framing
	4 Ea.	1" x 3"	Angle Braces
PLANT BOX NO. 3			
B	4	12" x 22"	Side
I	1	16" x 16"	Bottom
G	2	4½" x 10½"	Side of Base
G₁	2	4½" x 12"	Side of Base
J	1	10½" x 10½"	Bottom of Base
	8 Lin. ft.	1" x 2"	Top Framing
	5 Lin. ft.	2" x 2"	Bottom Framing
	4 Ea.	1" x 3"	Angle Braces

MISCELLANEOUS—(FOR ALL PLANT BOXES)
6d Finish Nails (ring shank or cement coated). Waterproof glue. Asphalt Emulsion or Coprus Lignum as required.

Table Planter

Build a simple table and eliminate patio balancing act by your guests

If you've ever tried to eat outdoors while balancing a drink and a plate of food, you can appreciate the need for a few strategically placed tables around the patio or terrace.

Here's a patio table which leads two lives. It has a small planter box on both ends, and a generous expanse of glass in between. You can put practically anything under the glass—your collection of sea shells, or a map of your favorite area. Put your plate and drink on top of the glass,

For decoration, hostess has taped a chart of seashore area to bottom of glass covering the table.

and you won't have to balance them on your knee any more.

The table can be made from one panel of ⅜-inch exterior-type fir plywood. The uprights come from one end of the panel, and the box area uses up the remainder. You can get inexpensive glass at hardware stores, lumberyards, or at your neighborhood retail glass store.

If you'd rather use the box area for storage of magazines and books, cover it with a solid panel of fir plywood. Either

way, the table is decorative and useful. It's equally at home inside the house when bad weather drives you indoors. With the right finish it is a decorative piece of furniture, that may be suitable for either living room or bedroom.

The sides, ends, and bottom of the box area fit together with butt joints, glued and nailed with light finishing nails. The sides of the box are nailed into the uprights.

Be sure to use exterior-type fir plywood if you plan to use the table on the patio. •

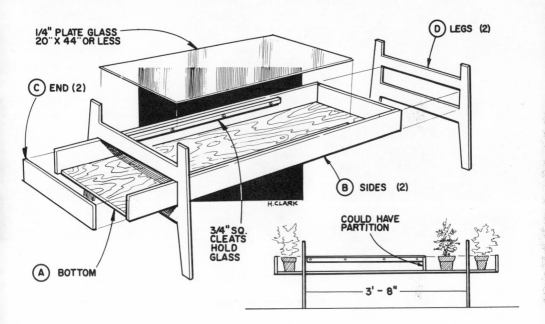

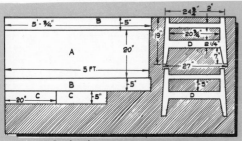

3/8"X 4' X 8' EXTERIOR PLYWOOD CUTS

Simple butt joints are specified for easy construction, and table was designed so that the box area fits tightly inside the upright legs.

Plaster Patching

Even the smallest crack must be filled before attempting to paint or wallpaper your room.

AS with so many home repair projects, thorough preparation pays dividends in patching cracks or holes in plastered walls and ceilings. Preparation for patching is the tedious part of the job and the handy man needs to be reminded not to give it the once-over-lightly treatment.

By preparation we mean the cleaning away of all loose bits of plaster from the area that is being repaired; also, the undercutting, or notching, that will give the patch a toehold; and the brushing away of the plaster dust.

Now, having said that, let's go on to say that the smallest patching jobs actually don't require much advance work. A dent or nick in a plastered wall needs only to be wiped clean with a cloth before being filled with a spackle-type compound. The same goes for tiny cracks which, while no wider than the proverbial hair, are wide enough to receive the compound. On the other

hand, the results will be smoother in cracks ⅛ inch wide if the edges are gently trimmed before filling. An excellent tool for this job is a beer can opener.

The best compound for these small jobs and for patching small holes in plaster is the kind that remains usable for up to three or four hours. If both large and small patches are to be made, tackle the small cracks and holes first to get the feel of it.

After you have cleaned the small crack or hole in the plaster, it is ready for the filling. A clean, old shallow dish or pie pan will serve well as your mixing bowl. Read the directions on the package of the compound and mix with water accordingly. Your "mud" should be smooth. Now, wet down the crack or hole with water immediately before putting in the plaster.

If it is a crack, work the compound into the crack with a putty knife. The wet mixture should be left just a trifle higher than

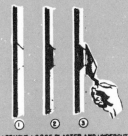

TO REPAIR A LARGE HOLE IN PLASTER
ON WOOD OR METAL LATH

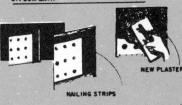

NEW PLASTER

NAILING STRIPS

1 REMOVE LOOSE PLASTER AND UNDERCUT
2 APPLY SCRATCH COAT.
3 APPLY FINISH WITH TROWEL

...AWAY THE OLD PLASTER FROM
...STING LATH. APPLY TWO COATS OF
...TER & ALLOW TO DRY THOROUGHLY
...GES OF PATCH MUST BE UNDERCUT

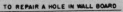

TO REPAIR A HOLE IN WALL BOARD

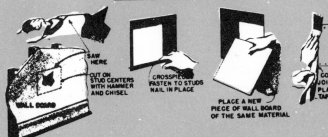

SAW
HERE

CUT ON
STUD CENTERS
WITH HAMMER
AND CHISEL

WALL BOARD

CROSSPIECES
FASTEN TO STUDS
NAIL IN PLACE

PLACE A NEW
PIECE OF WALL BOARD
OF THE SAME MATERIAL

CONCEAL
JOINTS WITH
PLASTER OVER
TAPE

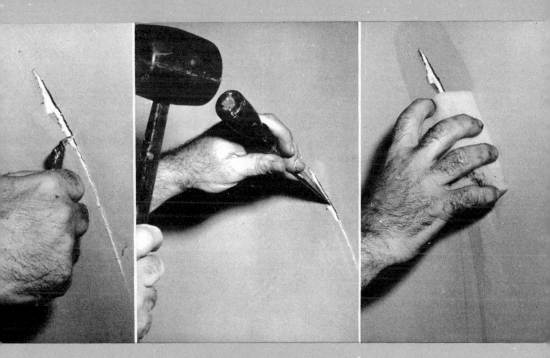

Photos above show preliminary steps in patching a small crack in a wall. Using a beer can opener or chisel, enlarge and deepen the opening. Also try to undercut to give better adhesion of new plaster. Brush area to clean out all dirt and loose particles. Soak with water just before putting on the plaster.

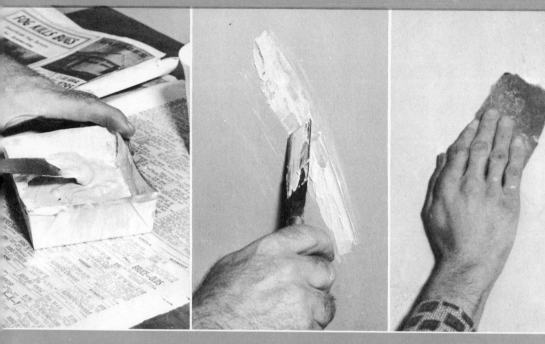

After preparatory work is done mix the plaster or spackle compound. Mix only the amount needed to fix the areas that are prepared to receive plaster. Apply with putty knife or small trowel, filling half the depth of crack. Let stand for 30 minutes and fill area completely. Sand patch even with adjacent wall.

When patch is dry, smooth and level, remove all dust and cover with coat of shellac or glue size.

On larger cracks or breaks use a chisel to remove all loose plaster before attempting repair.

the plaster around it. The patch will shrink a bit as it dries. If it still is too high after drying, use fine sandpaper to take it down to surface level. Wrap the sandpaper around a block of wood for this operation, making certain that the patch has thoroughly dried before sanding. This warning applies to all plaster patches.

In filling small holes, wet the area with water before applying the compound with putty knife or small trowel. For cracks of more than one eighth of an inch, larger holes and places where a good-sized chunk of plaster has dropped out, use patching plaster, a product sold under a number of brand names. In doing the job a wide-edged putty knife and a plasterer's trowel are necessary tools, and a clean paint brush is a handy instrument for applying water to the surfaces to which the plaster must adhere. The wetting helps bond the new to the old and it permits the patch to dry evenly without having the moisture around the edges absorbed into the surrounding wall.

A beer can opener will serve well to make the undercut around the edges, whether it be a crack or larger area. The idea is to make the area wider at the bottom than at the top. This gives the patch something extra to hang on to and prevents its falling out. Dust out the undercut area. Wetting down is next, but before proceeding, mix a batch of patching plaster, remembering not to prepare too large a quantity because it dries fast. Now quickly wet down the area and begin applying the plaster. Fill only to about one half the depth of wider cracks and holes, pressing the plaster in firmly. Do not smooth the surface of this first application. The second application, which will bring the level of the patch up to that of the surrounding area, will stick better to the first if it is rough.

We can think of it in terms of first and second coats. The first half fills the opening, the second brings it to the level of the surface and a trifle more to allow for shrinkage.

The first coat is now in; let it stand for about one hour, or until it is dry. Now repeat the mixing and wetting steps and apply the second coat. This time you want a smooth surface and one that feathers over the edges of the patch. Give it plenty of time to dry thoroughly—an hour at a minimum, overnight to play it safe.

You may find it has dried flush with the surrounding surface, or it may require a touch of sanding with fine sandpaper. Or, if not enough allowance was made for shrinkage, the patch may require a thin application of plaster to bring it level.

Once it is dry, smooth and level, the patch should be dusted, then brushed with a thin shellac or glue size to seal it. When dry, the surface is ready for painting. •

Materials needed for successful plaster repairs. Large float is used for the bigger jobs only.

Conversation Platform

No shouting across the room . . . guests are comfortably relaxed in modern, informal setting.

A RADICAL departure from the conventional design of a small house is suggested in this idea by architect Chris Choate. Inside a sheltering shell, he proposes regrouping of functions in island units of which a "conversation platform" is one. The object is to keep seating and circulation separated and marked by raising one area as is done here. Although this approach does not eliminate all conventional furniture in a room, it substitutes for an entire furniture grouping.

The platform in this setting consists of a ¾-inch plywood surface raised about 6 inches above the floor. Its main section is covered with an appropriate thick carpeting. On it is a slight elevation about 4x7 feet built from plywood, on which there is a low cushion of foam rubber forming a divan without arms or back. Next to it is a slightly higher horizontal plywood surface coming about level with the cushion surface that acts as a place to put things—cigarettes, ash tray, a magazine. The whole element is 12 feet square. It is mounted on a conventional frame concealed by 1-inch horizontal louvers that provide a patterned visual effect.

Above his conversation platform, Choate suggests an interior soffit that is tuned to the Oriental simplicity of his decor. This consists simply of a flat fir plywood surface hung from the ceiling inside exposed linear framing members. Worked out in good proportions, this adds to the beauty of the setting, provides a simple inexpensive method of indirect lighting and pulls the ceiling far enough down above the platform so its occupants will feel comfortable on their low seating elements. •

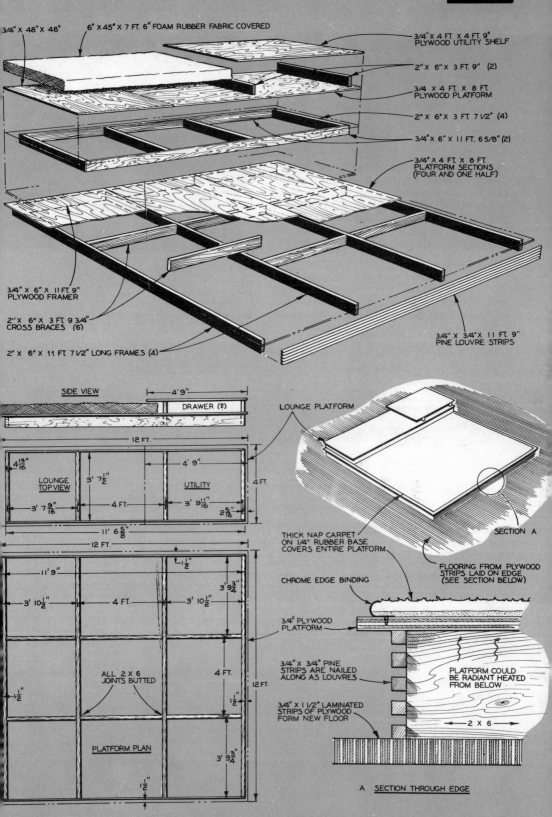

3/4" X 48" X 48"

6" X 45" X 7 FT. 6" FOAM RUBBER FABRIC COVERED

3/4" X 4 FT. X 4 FT. 9"
PLYWOOD UTILITY SHELF

2" X 6" X 3 FT. 9" (2)

3/4 X 4 FT. X 8 FT.
PLYWOOD PLATFORM

2" X 6" X 3 FT. 7 1/2" (4)

3/4" X 6" X 11 FT. 6 5/8" (2)

3/4" X 4 FT. X 8 FT.
PLATFORM SECTIONS
(FOUR AND ONE HALF)

3/4" X 6" X 11 FT. 9"
PLYWOOD FRAMER

2" X 6" X 3 FT. 9 3/4"
CROSS BRACES (6)

2" X 6" X 11 FT. 7 1/2" LONG FRAMES (4)

3/4" X 3/4" X 11 FT. 9"
PINE LOUVRE STRIPS

SIDE VIEW

4' 9"

DRAWER (?)

12 FT.

4 13/16"

LOUNGE
TOP VIEW

3' 7 1/2"

4' 9"

UTILITY

4 FT.

3' 7 9/16"

4 FT.

3' 9 11/16"

2 5/8"

11' 6 5/8"

12 FT.

11' 9"

1 1/2"

3' 9 3/4"

3' 10 1/2"

4 FT.

3' 10 1/2"

4 FT.

12 FT.

ALL 2 X 6
JOINTS BUTTED

1 1/2"

1 1/2"

PLATFORM PLAN

3' 9 3/4"

1 1/2"

LOUNGE PLATFORM

THICK NAP CARPET
ON 1/4" RUBBER BASE
COVERS ENTIRE PLATFORM

SECTION A

FLOORING FROM PLYWOOD
STRIPS LAID ON EDGE
(SEE SECTION BELOW)

CHROME EDGE BINDING

3/4" PLYWOOD
PLATFORM

PLATFORM COULD
BE RADIANT HEATED
FROM BELOW

3/4" X 3/4" PINE
STRIPS ARE NAILED
ALONG AS LOUVRES

2 X 6

3/4" X 1 1/2" LAMINATED
STRIPS OF PLYWOOD
FORM NEW FLOOR

A   SECTION THROUGH EDGE

2209

Children's Play Areas

Provide for your youngster's pleasure with a play area of his own that plans for easy supervision and safety as well.

AS ONE SAGE aptly put it, "Children are a great comfort in your old age—and they help you get there faster." This is particularly true when little or no provision has been made for their pleasure. They rate a place of their own where they can romp and play to their heart's content, entertain their friends and give full rein to their energies and resourcefulness.

Children are an imaginative lot and will tire quickly of toys or equipment that can only be used "as-is" and do not lend themselves to imaginative byplay. The con-

ventional swings, teeter-totter, slide, monkey bars, etc., are excellent body-builders and will get good use, but with them should be included certain other forms of equipment.

For instance, a 6-foot length of 30-inch concrete or stock steel pipe, mounted on a concrete or wooden cradle, will give the kids more fun than a barrel of monkeys. They can crawl through it in follow-the-leader games, hide in it, ride it as a horse one day and a rocket ship the next. They will never tire of concocting new and fan-

ciful uses for it. A number of these, laid out in zig-zag formation about the play area, will make perfect accessories and enable the young mind to amaze you with its inventiveness.

Another item that lends itself nicely to a variety of games is the simple playhouse and toy storage designed by landscape architect Warren E. Lauesen. This open-sided, box-shaped structure will serve the children as a play house, a country store, a refreshment stand, a hide-out for "Jesse James," a hoosegow, a clubhouse. You give them the basic structure; they'll provide the imagination.

More elaborate play equipment can be provided in the form of a large plywood mock-up of a cabin cruiser, a rocket ship, an airplane, or any similar type of vehicle which the kids can navigate across imaginary oceans or through outer space. The play boat designed by Warren E. Lauesen

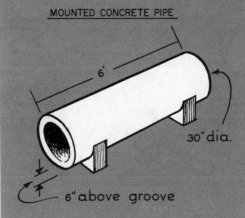

MOUNTED CONCRETE PIPE

6'

30" dia.

6" above groove

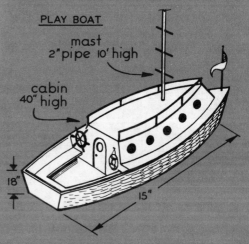

PLAY BOAT

mast
2" pipe 10' high

cabin
40" high

18"

15"

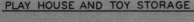

PLAY HOUSE AND TOY STORAGE

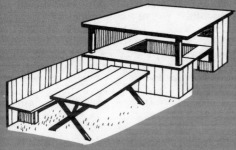

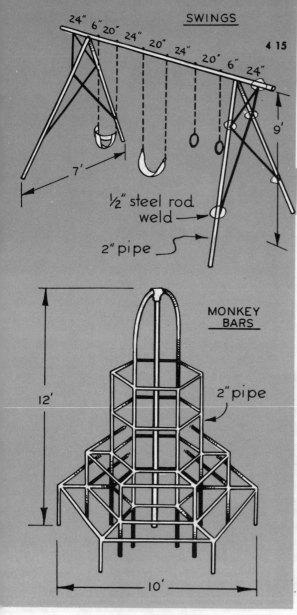

24" 6" 20" 24" 20" 24" 20" 6" 24"

9'

7'

½" steel rod weld

2" pipe

MONKEY BARS

2" pipe

12'

10'

can be built of ¾-inch outdoor plywood and provided with a 10-foot high mast of 2-inch galvanized pipe as shown, which would be sturdy enough for the children to climb. Dimensions and design details are flexible and can be altered or fashioned to suit individual requirements.

If you don't want to build a vehicle mock-up, you can pick up an old car body at the junk yard, clean it up and paint it in gay, bright colors and let the kids take over from there.

Playthings such as slides, swings, monkey bars, etc., that encourage children to jump, fall, tumble, or make violent contact with the ground in any way, should be mounted on sand to give the kids something soft to land on. A good way to do this is to scoop the ground away to a depth of about 6 inches in the area allocated to these gymnastic items, and fill the section to its original level with sand. If desired, a redwood border of 1x6 can be laid out to enclose the sandy area.

Another provision for the pleasure of playing children is a paved area on which they can ride their vehicles or use their skates. For skating, this area should be smoothly paved with concrete, but for bikes, trikes, and kiddie cars, blacktop is adequate. For variety and artistic landscaping, this paved area can be in the form of a winding road, or a large circular race track surrounding a circular sandbox or sand area containing gymnastic equipment. If space permits, you can pave a figure-8 track encircling two sand areas.

Sand is one of the most versatile playthings for kids. The little ones play with it; the big ones romp in it. For the tiny tot, a small sandbox is adequate and one of pleasing design can be built that will not only serve its recreational purpose, but will also add to the landscaping decor. Two in-

Large play area by architects Leone and Wemple has swings, jungle gym, on decomposed granite.

Architect Warren Lauesen, for his own back yard, has patio, lawn, aviary and a play area behind.

teresting design possibilities are shown in diagrams. Made of 2x12 and 2x10 redwood, they feature combination sandboxes and bench areas which add to their functional value and attractiveness. In the design by landscape artist, Alexander Prentice, the bench area is widened and extended on one side to form a table surface on which toys can be placed while not in use. In the second design, the bench border takes a circuitous route around the angular sand-box, enclosing a small play area and giving the kids a long narrow platform on which they can walk and practice balancing.

When paving a large patio, a small cir-cular, rectangular or free-form opening can be left at one corner or in the middle to be later excavated to a depth of 6 inches and filled with sand for a sandbox. Sand that gets out of this area onto the paving can be easily swept back, and when the child outgrows the sandbox, it can be converted into a planter. Some of the decorative redwood sandboxes can also be converted to planters after they've served their time as toys.

Children love to imitate and you can di-rect this trait along constructive paths by giving them a means of keeping their toy vehicles in orderly fashion. To do this, simply provide a miniature parking lot, fashioned after the commercial variety found near super-markets and other large business establishments. Anchor a length of 2x2 redwood or similar rot-resistant wood to the ground alongside the play house or play area by driving long redwood stakes into the ground and nailing the border strip to them. Next, paint a series of parallel white lines on the ground, diag-onally away from this wooden strip to in-dicate parking stalls for the various trikes, bikes, and miniature cars to be parked there. This will not only encourage your

Sand-filled play area on hillside has lattice fence along steep side as protection, utilizes spare space.

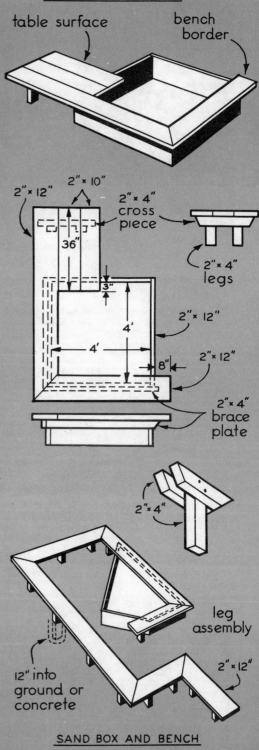

REDWOOD SAND BOX

table surface

bench border

2" × 12"

2" × 10"

2" × 4" cross piece

36"

2" × 4" legs

3"

2" × 12"

4'

4'

8"

2" × 12"

2" × 4" brace plate

2" × 4"

leg assembly

12" into ground or concrete

2" × 12"

SAND BOX AND BENCH

Children love a house of their own as headquarters for innumerable invented games. Fairytale playhouse shown here is in the California yard of bandleader Horace Heidt. Note shutters and planter window-box.

PARKING LOT FOR TOY VEHICLES

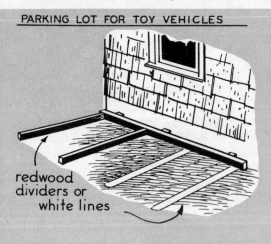

redwood dividers or white lines

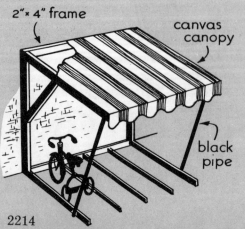

2" x 4" frame

canvas canopy

black pipe

children to park their vehicles in orderly fashion, but will also be an inducement for visiting juvenile firemen to follow suit. For protection against rain, etc., a canopy of canvas, wood, or reinforced Fiberglas plastic panels can be erected over the parking area.

Aside from the type and variety of play equipment needed to keep a kid happy and busy, an important factor to consider when laying out a children's play area is its location in the landscaping theme and its relationship to the family's way of outdoor living. The play area should be separated from the grown-ups' outdoor area, yet not so much that the children will be isolated and out of sight. You'll want to be able to keep an eye on the youngsters and they'll want you to watch their antics during special performances, which is only natural. If you don't want sand tracked onto your patio and into the house, separate the sand-box or sand area from the patio by a fair expanse of lawn which will wipe the sand off little feet. Grass won't grow where children play, so instead of trying to nurse a lawn in such areas, it will be easier to pave the section with black top or decomposed granite. Aim for a design that can be converted to grown-up use after children have outgrown the area. •

The late comedian Bob Burns of Bazooka fame had this trolley-ride children's delight in his yard. After mounting steps, as diagramed below, youngster holds on to runner and makes aerial ride across the lawn.

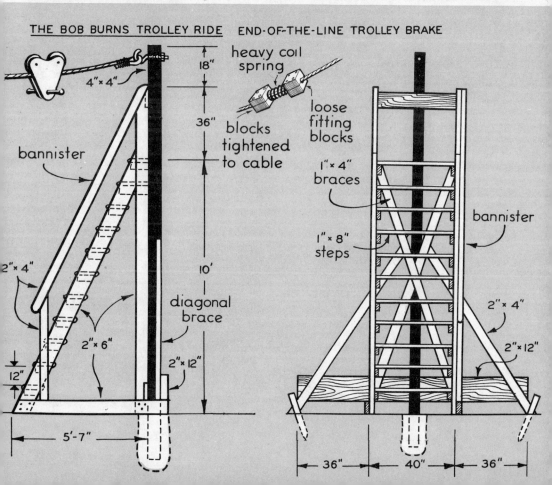

THE BOB BURNS TROLLEY RIDE   END-OF-THE-LINE TROLLEY BRAKE

4" × 4"

18"

heavy coil spring

36"

blocks tightened to cable

loose fitting blocks

bannister

1" × 4" braces

1" × 8" steps

bannister

2" × 4"

10'

diagonal brace

2" × 6"

2" × 12"

2" × 4"

2" × 12"

12"

5'-7"

36"   40"   36"

Play Area

by Emil Brodbeck

It's sturdy, safe, and inexpensive to build.

MOST backyards, lots, etc., can be adapted to hold a play area like this one. It features a swing, slide, teeter-totter, sandbox and pool area. Construction is detailed in diagrams on next few pages. Study carefully.

EIGHTEEN-INCH bases of three main upright members of swing structure are heavily creosoted to protect them when in ground. Do this twice, saturating them completely.

UPRIGHTS are checked with level after being set in 18-inch holes. Structure is wedged in proper position with rocks, checked for accuracy, and then cemented.

LET cement dry two days, then put cross-brace on one side of the two uprights which form trapeze and swing area. Then put another cross piece between the two uprights.

LARGE clamp holds boards together. Large bit is used to drill through facing boards and upright at either side, and through facing boards and core board, as shown.

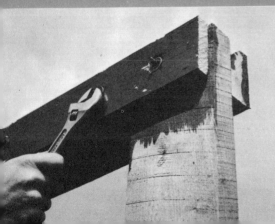

CLOSEUP shows how facing boards are bolted to uprights on either side. Nut is fastened on bolt which runs through facing board and core board inside upright area, as shown.

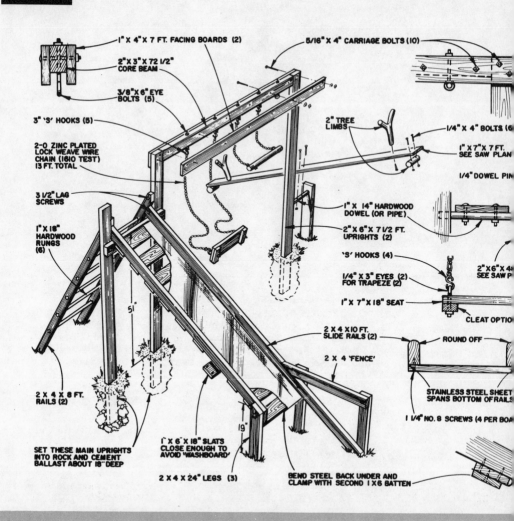

1" X 4" X 7 FT. FACING BOARDS (2)

2" X 3" X 72 1/2" CORE BEAM

3/8" X 6" EYE BOLTS (5)

3" 'S' HOOKS (5)

2-0 ZINC PLATED LOCK WEAVE WIRE CHAIN (1610 TEST) 13 FT. TOTAL

3 1/2" LAG SCREWS

1" X 18" HARDWOOD RUNGS (6)

51"

2 X 4 X 8 FT. RAILS (2)

SET THESE MAIN UPRIGHTS INTO ROCK AND CEMENT BALLAST ABOUT 18" DEEP

1" X 6" X 18" SLATS CLOSE ENOUGH TO AVOID 'WASHBOARD'

19"

2 X 4 X 24" LEGS (3)

5/16" X 4" CARRIAGE BOLTS (10)

2" TREE LIMBS

1/4" X 4" BOLTS (6

1" X 7" X 7 FT. SEE SAW PLAN

1/4" DOWEL PIN

1" X 14" HARDWOOD DOWEL (OR PIPE)

2" X 6" X 7 1/2 FT. UPRIGHTS (2)

'S' HOOKS (4)

1/4" X 3" EYES (2) FOR TRAPEZE (2)

1" X 7" X 18" SEAT

2" X 6" X 4 SEE SAW P

CLEAT OPTION

ROUND OFF

2 X 4 X 10 FT. SLIDE RAILS (2)

2 X 4 'FENCE'

STAINLESS STEEL SHEET SPANS BOTTOM OF RAILS

1 1/4" NO. 8 SCREWS (4 PER BOA

BEND STEEL BACK UNDER AND CLAMP WITH SECOND 1 X 6 BATTEN

SLIDE is made from two 10-foot 2x4s nailed together temporarily while piece of 8-foot stainless steel and slats are nailed in place. See the diagram above for construction.

LADDER handrails are nailed in place temporarily while holes are drilled. Then handrails are bolted in place securely. See diagram for placement of handrails.

WITH handrails bolted in place, ends of bolts are sawed off. Secure bolts tightly, make sure they will not come loose later.

ABOUT five feet up from base of uprights, tops of the handrails are cut off, as shown in the photograph. Do not cut into uprights.

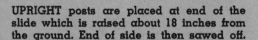

UPRIGHT posts are placed at end of the slide which is raised about 18 inches from the ground. End of side is then sawed off.

SMALL "fence" is then added to end of slide; a 2x4 is securely bolted to top of post at slide end, as shown in the diagram.

EDGE of "fence" is cut at angle, then all ends are sanded smooth and rounded to help prevent any injury. Length of fence will keep children out of the swing area.

HOLES to accommodate "eye" bolts are drilled. "Eye" bolts hold "S" hooks for the swing and the trapeze. Two swings and one trapeze then can be fitted on this structure.

3/4" X 4 FT. X 6 FT. EXTERIOR
PLYWOOD HINGED PLATFORM

2 X 4 EDGE CLEATS

'T' OR STRAP HINGES,
OR OLD PIANO HINGE

NOTCH
OVER
BOLT

HANK CLARK

CUT 2 X 4 TO
CLEAR ROCKS

ROCKS SET
INTO BASE
OF SAND

SAND PLAY PIT

4" WIDE SECTION OF
PLYWOOD BOLTED
TO ROCKS

2 X 4 X 44"
PLATFORM JOIST

3/8" X 6" BOLT SET
INTO MORTAR WHEN
JOINING ROCKS

6" X 46" LOGS (2) (OR 2 X 4'S)
CREOSOTED BELOW GROUND

HEAVY manila rope is passed through eye bolt and tied tightly. Rope is knotted to make climbing easier. Kids will love it.

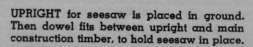

STRAIGHT tree branch makes fine trapeze. Board about 18 inches long, 5 5/7 inches wide and ¾ inch thick makes swing seat.

CARPENTER'S level is used to mark off location of steps for ladder. First rung is even with top of slide. Drill holes for rungs.

HEAVY dowels are used for rungs. Rungs are driven through holes in handrails from either side, as indicated in the photograph.

UPRIGHT for seesaw is placed in ground. Then dowel fits between upright and main construction timber, to hold seesaw in place.

HEAVY crotch section of tree limb is screwed to seesaw. It serves as handles for children to hang onto when seesawing.

WHOLE structure of play area is heavily creosoted. It's easier on clothing and hands if the seats and handles are painted, too.

SANDBOX is made by placing rocks in base of sand, as shown in the photo above and in the diagram at top, across the page.

TOP of sandbox is cemented; smaller "wedge" rocks are cemented into place, too. Don't cement lower rocks, allow drainage.

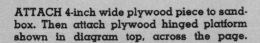

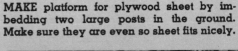

ATTACH 4-inch wide plywood piece to sandbox. Then attach plywood hinged platform shown in diagram top, across the page.

MAKE platform for plywood sheet by imbedding two large posts in the ground. Make sure they are even so sheet fits nicely.

BACKYARD PLAYGROUND

MONKEY BARS were made using 3x3″ posts but 4x4s may also be used. Sand all pieces to eliminate rough edges then varnish or paint.

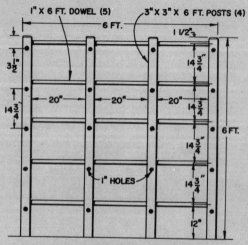

1″ X 6 FT. DOWEL (5) 3″ X 3″ X 6 FT. POSTS (4)

6 FT.

1 1/2″

3 1/2″

14 3/4″

20″ 20″ 20″

14 3/4″

14 3/4″

14 3/4″

1″ HOLES

6 FT.

12″

MAKE FOUR GRID ASSEMBLIES SAME AS THIS

By Walter Ian Fischman

These well-designed outdoor toys are simple, inexpensive.

FOR THE FAMILY with two or more children, the safest way to know what they're doing in the playground is to bring the playground to the children.

The selection of wooden outdoor toys shown on these pages are at least a be ginning for a very safe and suitable play area for your back yard, and are not expensive to build. Standard lumber was used throughout, as well as simple procedure. One would not need a fully equipped workshop to do this project well. Detailed drawings and clear pho tographs will supply all the information needed. Note clever designs as well as sturdy construction. •

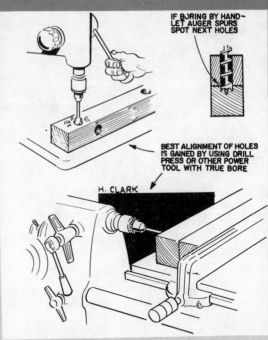

IF BORING BY HAND— LET AUGER SPURS SPOT NEXT HOLES

BEST ALIGNMENT OF HOLES IS GAINED BY USING DRILL PRESS OR OTHER POWER TOOL WITH TRUE BORE

H. CLARK

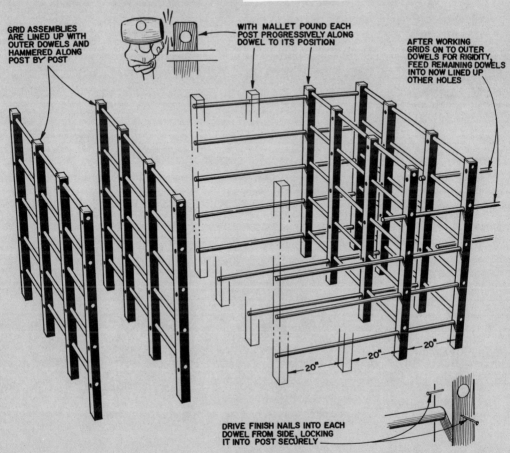

GRID ASSEMBLIES ARE LINED UP WITH OUTER DOWELS AND HAMMERED ALONG POST BY POST

WITH MALLET POUND EACH POST PROGRESSIVELY ALONG DOWEL TO ITS POSITION

AFTER WORKING GRIDS ON TO OUTER DOWELS FOR RIGIDITY, FEED REMAINING DOWELS INTO NOW LINED UP OTHER HOLES

20" 20" 20"

DRIVE FINISH NAILS INTO EACH DOWEL FROM SIDE, LOCKING IT INTO POST SECURELY

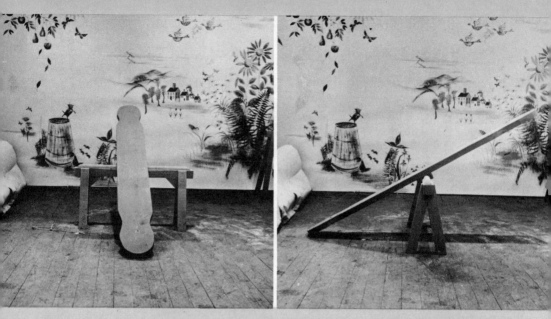

SEESAW shown on this page was made with 7-ft. 2x8-in. plank set on simple sawhorse. Round top of 2-in. half-round molding on top permits smooth ride. Wax underside of top.

●

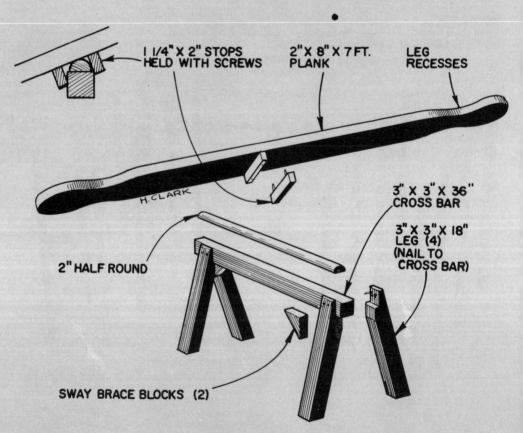

1 1/4" X 2" STOPS HELD WITH SCREWS

2" X 8" X 7 FT. PLANK

LEG RECESSES

H. CLARK

3" X 3" X 36" CROSS BAR

3" X 3" X 18" LEG (4) (NAIL TO CROSS BAR)

2" HALF ROUND

SWAY BRACE BLOCKS (2)

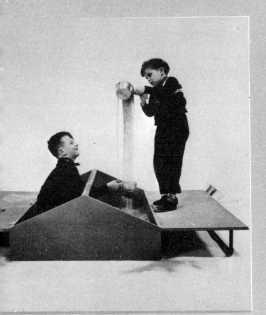

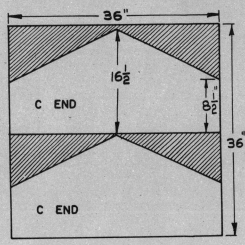

36"

16½"

C END

8½"

C END

36"

1/2" EXTERIOR PLYWOOD

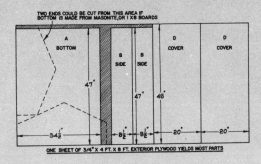

TWO ENDS COULD BE CUT FROM THIS AREA IF
BOTTOM IS MADE FROM MASONITE, OR 1 X 8 BOARDS

A BOTTOM

B SIDE

B SIDE

D COVER

D COVER

47"

47"

48"

34½"

8½"

8½"

20"

20"

ONE SHEET OF 3/4" X 4 FT. X 8 FT. EXTERIOR PLYWOOD YIELDS MOST PARTS

CLEVERLY-DESIGNED sand box has folding top to keep out weather, neighborhood pets; keeps children up off the ground.

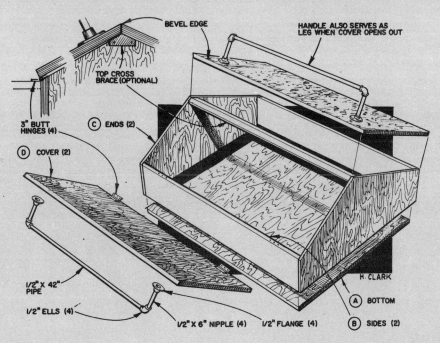

BEVEL EDGE

HANDLE ALSO SERVES AS
LEG WHEN COVER OPENS OUT

TOP CROSS
BRACE (OPTIONAL)

3" BUTT
HINGES (4)

C ENDS (2)

D COVER (2)

1/2" X 42"
PIPE

1/2" ELLS (4)

1/2" X 6" NIPPLE (4)

1/2" FLANGE (4)

A BOTTOM

B SIDES (2)

H. CLARK

2225

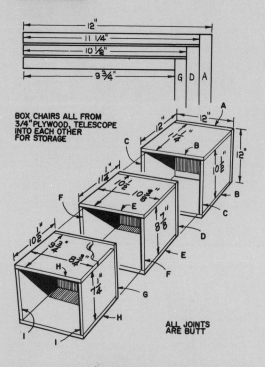

BOX CHAIRS ALL FROM
3/4"PLYWOOD, TELESCOPE
INTO EACH OTHER
FOR STORAGE

ALL JOINTS
ARE BUTT

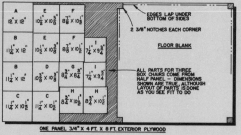

A 12" X 12"	E 10½" X 10½"	F 8⅝" X 10½"	EDGES LAP UNDER BOTTOM OF SIDES
B 11¼" X 12"	E 10½" X 10½"	F 8⅝" X 10½"	2 3/8" NOTCHES EACH CORNER FLOOR BLANK
B 11¼" X 12"	D 10⅝" X 10½"	G 8¾" X 8¾"	H 8¼" X 10½"
C 11¼" X 10½"	C 11¼" X 10½"	H 8¾" X 10½"	H 8¾" X 10½"

ALL PARTS FOR THREE
BOX CHAIRS COME FROM
HALF PANEL — DIMENSIONS
SHOWN ARE TRUE, ALTHOUGH
LAYOUT OF PARTS IS DONE
AS YOU SEE FIT TO DO

F 8⅝" X 10½" F 7¼" X 9¾" G 8¾" X 8¾" I 7¼" X 9¾"

ONE PANEL 3/4" X 4 FT. X 8 FT. EXTERIOR PLYWOOD

SAND BOX TABLE is raised off ground, has Masonite top to protect sand, act as table.

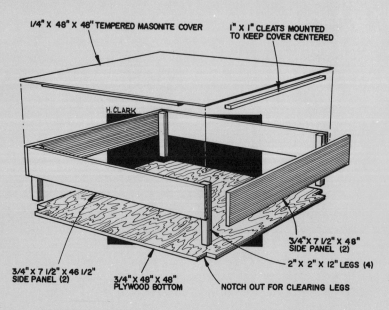

1/4" X 48" X 48" TEMPERED MASONITE COVER

1" X 1" CLEATS MOUNTED
TO KEEP COVER CENTERED

H. CLARK

3/4"X 7 1/2" X 48"
SIDE PANEL (2)

2" X 2" X 12" LEGS (4)

3/4" X 7 1/2" X 46 1/2"
SIDE PANEL (2)

3/4" X 48" X 48"
PLYWOOD BOTTOM

NOTCH OUT FOR CLEARING LEGS

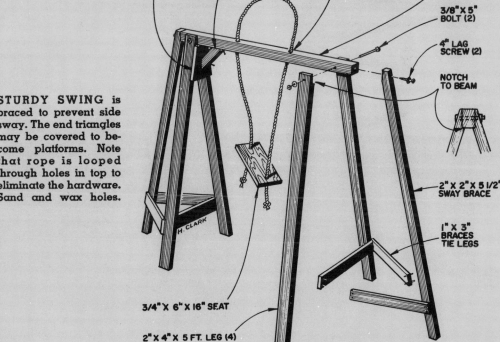

1" X 8" GUSSET

2" X 2" BRACE

1/2" ROPE OF LENGTH TO SUIT SIZE OF CHILD —THROUGH TWO 5/8" HOLES

3" X 3" X 5 FT. (OR 2 X 4) CROSS BEAM

3/8" X 5" BOLT (2)

4" LAG SCREW (2)

NOTCH TO BEAM

2" X 2" X 5 1/2" SWAY BRACE

1" X 3" BRACES TIE LEGS

3/4" X 6" X 16" SEAT

2" X 4" X 5 FT. LEG (4)

H. CLARK

STURDY SWING is braced to prevent side sway. The end triangles may be covered to become platforms. Note that rope is looped through holes in top to eliminate the hardware. Sand and wax holes.

2227

children's play equipment

If you build units yourself they can be expansive and yet not expensive.

CHILDREN REQUIRE an outdoor play area as much as they need space for play indoors. The best place to have it is in view of the rooms from which it's most convenient to watch them. A play area is especially good outside their bedrooms, playroom, or near a family room.

A southern exposure is best in most cases, for it can get sun all day, yet be shaded when the sun isn't wanted. A tree is one of the most pleasant ways to get shade, and it may also be used for climbing, to support swings, or a tree house.

Plan to protect the area from annoying prevailing winds, and if you can, provide a play shed or other shelter for rainy days. A fence around the play area will mean less supervision. Also, children like to know they are secure, and an enclosure helps give them that feeling.

A hard surface is needed for wheeled toys. In planning walks, design them with curves, not angles. A tricycle circle, or run, can give countless hours of fun. You need soft surfaces where they are most likely to fall. A lawn is the place for tumbling and wrestling. If you can, get tanbark. Grass or tanbark is especially important under climbing equipment, but don't expect grass to take hard wear and concentrated abuse. If the play area is small, pavement is needed. Brick or patio blocks set on sand are good nonskid surfaces.

Equip your play yard well. Children will want to stay in it only if they have fun there and plenty to keep them busy. The best facilities will cost very little if you provide them yourself, and you will find

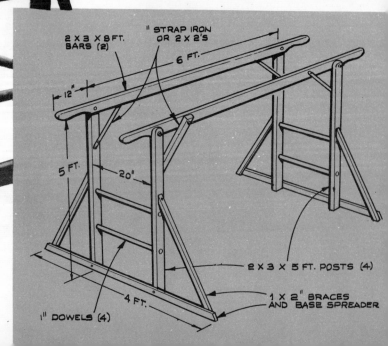

2 X 3 X 8 FT. BARS (2)

1" STRAP IRON OR 2 X 2'S

6 FT.

12"

5 FT.

20"

2 X 3 X 5 FT. POSTS (4)

1 X 2" BRACES AND BASE SPREADER

4 FT.

1" DOWELS (4)

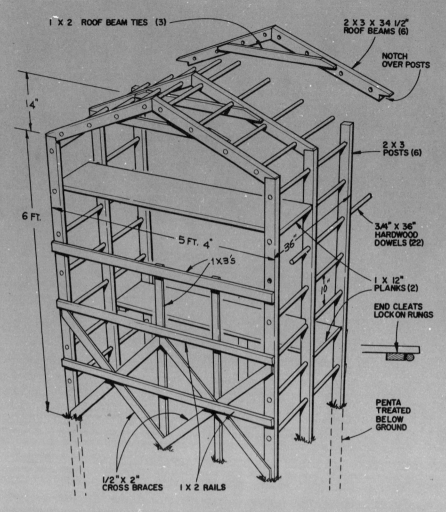

1 X 2 ROOF BEAM TIES (3)

2 X 3 X 34 1/2" ROOF BEAMS (6)

NOTCH OVER POSTS

14"

2 X 3 POSTS (6)

6 FT.

5 FT. 4"

36"

3/4" X 36" HARDWOOD DOWELS (22)

1 X 3'S

10"

1 X 12" PLANKS (2)

END CLEATS LOCK ON RUNGS

PENTA TREATED BELOW GROUND

1/2" X 2" CROSS BRACES

1 X 2 RAILS

This climber can be converted to rose arbor or vine support after usefulness for play is over.

Stanley clamps make strong sawhorses which can be used to support Ping-pong, other game tables.

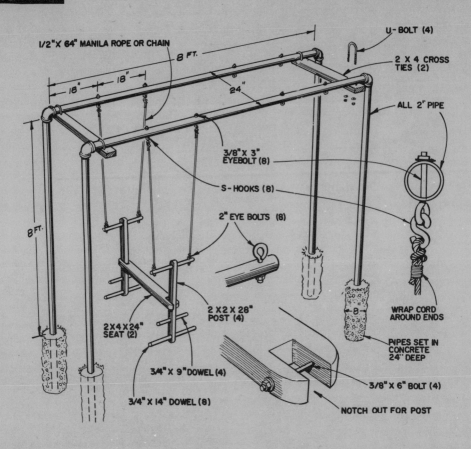

1/2" X 64" MANILA ROPE OR CHAIN

8 FT.

18"

18"

24"

8 FT.

U - BOLT (4)

2 X 4 CROSS TIES (2)

ALL 2" PIPE

3/8" X 3" EYEBOLT (8)

S - HOOKS (8)

2" EYE BOLTS (8)

2 X 2 X 28" POST (4)

2 X 4 X 24" SEAT (2)

3/4" X 9" DOWEL (4)

3/4" X 14" DOWEL (8)

WRAP CORD AROUND ENDS

PIPES SET IN CONCRETE 24" DEEP

3/8" X 6" BOLT (4)

NOTCH OUT FOR POST

Swings are safer if you make it difficult for children to dart in front of them. See drawing.

Cargo-net climber is simple, inexpensively made. Throw a tarpaulin over it and it becomes a tent.

that it is the simplest things which children love most.

Dirt and sand boxes. Young children will want to dig. It can be in dirt or sand. They get more pleasure and satisfaction from it than almost anything else. A skimpy sandbox isn't enough. What they really like are huge mountains of sand into which they can tunnel. Sand is cheap. A cover may be necessary to protect it from fouling by pets.

Next to dirt, children like "mud" best, and a good mud hole can be pure joy. If you want to make them happy, provide a faucet for their use in making mud and in washing dirty hands. Combine the faucet with a drinking fountain, and you'll eliminate the need for troops of thirsty, grimy rascals to invade the kitchen and use up all the clean glasses.

Children enjoy a "hill." If your yard is flat, you may find it desirable to pile up dirt to make such a play hill. If you have any occasion to excavate, save the dirt for this purpose, plant it with grass.

Low-cost fun. The best play equipment can often be made of scraps, leftovers, and other waste materials. Sturdy boxes are perfect for climbing, building, and all sorts of imaginative play. Planks can become ramps for getting up on the boxes or can serve as bridges between them. An accompanying sketch shows how to make boxes which are indestructible.

An old automobile tire sliced through the middle can become a circular waterway on which to sail tiny boats. Hung from a tree, it can be a swing. You can attach it to the rope at one point or, better yet, at three. Tying it at three places makes it a flat seat.

A durable outdoor blackboard can be made by painting Masonite with chalkboard paint, available at your paint store, or with ordinary paint to which emery dust has been added.

Climbers. Climbing is a favorite pastime. A climber patterned after an Army commando climber is easy to build. Use rope to make the net, or get a regular cargo net, available from marine supply outlets. Instead of rope, the "net" can be 6x6-inch welded wire fabric, of the type used in reinforcing concrete. Give it an undercoat of red lead primer to keep it from rusting. Throw a tarp or blanket over the climber, and the children can enjoy it as a tent.

Children grow fast, and elaborate equipment can soon become useless, so it is often wise to plan for convertibility. Accompanying photo and diagram show a climber which can become a rose arbor.

One of the best climbers is a make-believe house. This need be no more than a roof set on four stout cedar posts. Ramps, ladders, or other means of getting up on the roof are what make the house so much fun. The real thrill is sitting up on the roof ridge. It can amuse children for hours, where more sophisticated equipment won't hold them for minutes.

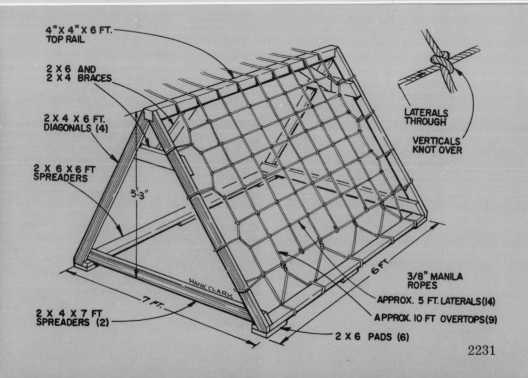

4" X 4" X 6 FT. TOP RAIL

2 X 6 AND 2 X 4 BRACES

2 X 4 X 6 FT. DIAGONALS (4)

2 X 6 X 6 FT SPREADERS

5'-3"

HANK CLARK

7 FT.

2 X 4 X 7 FT SPREADERS (2)

2 X 6 PADS (6)

LATERALS THROUGH

VERTICALS KNOT OVER

6 FT.

3/8" MANILA ROPES

APPROX. 5 FT. LATERALS (14)

APPROX. 10 FT OVERTOPS (9)

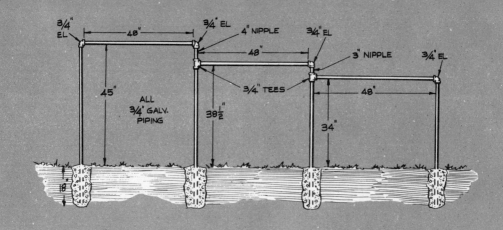

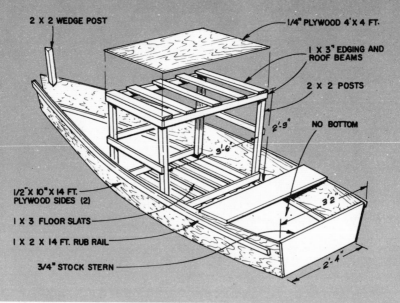

1/4" PLYWOOD 4'x 4 FT.

1 X 3" EDGING AND ROOF BEAMS

2 X 2 POSTS

2 X 2 WEDGE POST

NO BOTTOM

2'-9"

3'-6"

3'-2"

1/2" X 10" X 14 FT. PLYWOOD SIDES (2)

1 X 3 FLOOR SLATS

1 X 2 X 14 FT. RUB RAIL

3/4" STOCK STERN

2'-4"

Seven pieces of galvanized pipe and half a dozen fittings can be assembled into multiple gym bar.

This make-believe boat will never float, but will provide many fun hours for boys and girls alike.

A variety of climbing arrangements can be made using galvanized pipe. Pipe can be bought for a fraction of its new cost at building-wrecker and at junk yards. If you don't have your own thread cutter, you can usually have threads cut at the plumbers at about 10 cents per threaded end. New ¾-inch galvanized pipe costs approximately 20 cents per foot at Sears Roebuck, plus 7 cents for each threaded end. All pipe and fittings for the steel-pipe gym illustrated cost under $8.00.

Slides and swings. Slides have their place among home play equipment items, but their success is often less than anticipated. They are likely to be a source of friction between children, and often are a hazard. Swings are far more rewarding, and are a real essential.

Commercial home swing equipment is usually scaled too small for any but the preschool child. Even tiny tots may find these swings placed too closely together Almost any hardware store carries the eyebolts, swivels, bearings, and chain, or rope, rope clamps, and rope thimbles needed to make your own swings. Sears offers an entire kit for two chain-supported swings at under $7.00.

To avoid squabbles, provide swings not only for your own children, but for play-mates as well. Support for swings can be a 2x6 or 2x8, attached between two trees. If you have only one tree, a pair of braced 2x4's can hold up the second end, or the wall of garage or house can also serve. You can often buy used 2- or 3-inch galvanized pipe at the junk yard, and set them in con-crete to make remarkably sturdy swing supports. In some localities, the telephone company not only gives away used poles but will drop them off at your home. A pair of poles, and crossarms, are all that you need to solve your swing-support prob-lems. Space swings a minimum of 18 inches apart.

For safety, block off the area around the swings so that children can't readily run in front of them. Where swings are for chil-dren too young to swing themselves, set the swings at a height well above that of toddler's heads. Swings are also easier to push at that level.

Don't be too realistic. The best play de-vices stimulate the imagination, so don't get too tight on details. A twisted piece of driftwood mounted on legs, to a child, can be a horse, a dragon, or a jet airplane. You need only a steering wheel, salvaged at a wrecker's lot, and something to sit on in front of it, to have an automobile.

An invariable favorite of children is a make-believe boat. It need not have a bot-tom, as the accompanying illustrations demonstrate, to be a success. Its design can be varied or improved upon, as available materials allow. Roof and sides, for ex-ample, can be made of Masonite. Masonite is easily flexed, is weatherproof, doesn't require painting, but it will take paint beautifully.

You'll need storage for toys to protect them from the weather and to keep them out of sight when not in use. A locker may serve your purposes. A bench can have a lift-up lid with storage under it. Put the bench where it can separate a paved area from grass and it can help keep wheeled toys where they belong. •

mks and boxes stimulate imaginative play as own. Details for "child-proof" box at right.

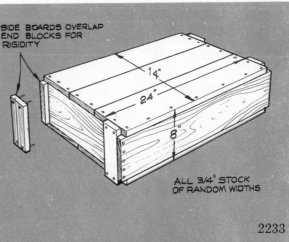

SIDE BOARDS OVERLAP
END BLOCKS FOR
RIGIDITY

14"

24"

8"

ALL ¾" STOCK
OF RANDOM WIDTHS

Play house as pictured here can be built mostly of scraps, or with leftovers from home building.

play houses and tree houses

How to supply low-cost high adventure—in your own back yard.

THERE ARE TWO WAYS to build a play house. One is to make it a neat, well-put-together structure that can continue to serve as a tool and garden storehouse after the children have outgrown it. It can be a miniature replica of your own house, and be as simple or elaborate as you want to make it.

The other way is to build it as a more imaginative and stimulating structure designed only for the temporary purpose of giving pleasure to children. It can have steps and ladders, secret entrances, trapdoors, and be thoroughly unconventional and nonsensical in design. Children will love to "help" build either type of play house.

Both boys and girls enjoy play houses.

Boys can use it as a club hideout and meeting place. Girls will use it to set up make-believe housekeeping. Either can use it to play store, school, fortress, etc., and it can always serve to keep children and toys out of the rain.

Size. The play house should be large enough to sleep in. It can be made to look more imposing, and have extra practicality, if you include a separate section or room for tool or other storage. If the play house includes a carport or garage, it may be large enough to shelter your new small car. Otherwise its pint-size garage or carport can be used for those countless wheeled toys. In some areas, your play house may find increased use if it includes a screened porch. Other possible features include a

Scrap 1 inch boards are used to sheathe walls which are framed with 2x4's on 32-inch centers.

A play house, unlike any real house, stimulates children's imaginations, has much to recommend it.

The Hansel-and-Gretel trim and simulated chimney give this play house a storybook appearance.

"Shingled" roof is actually made of long strips of Masonite, lapped at each course (shown above).

second story, or an attic. If you are venturesome, you may want to attempt a split-level design. Fanciful Hansel-and-Gretel storybook architecture may also find favor with the children.

Support. An 8x16-inch pier foundation made of concrete blocks is substantial enough for almost any size play house. Fill the blocks with concrete (or Sakrete Gravel Mix) to give them extra weight, and fasten a 2x6 sill to them with a ½x8-inch anchor bolt. Two or three blocks below grade are usually enough. The blocks need not rest on a footing. Use Mortar Mix for cementing the blocks together.

Another good method of support is with standard fence posts, of cedar, redwood, or preservative-treated fir. A third possibility is to put the house on a concrete slab. Use 6 inches of gravel under the slab.

Floor. For spans up to 8 feet, the house

Extension at rear of playhouse can be a garage for a small car, or a shelter for wheeled toys.

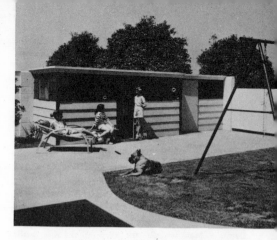

Playhouse designed and built by architect Wahl Snyder for his Miami Shores home features porch.

Play house coordinated as part of children's own terrace, play area, has separate storage section.

Materials cost for this house, built of all new stock, was approximately $125. Details are below.

floor structure can be of 2x4-inch joists on 16 to 24-inch centers. The floor will be too springy if it spans more than 8 feet, so go to 2x6's, or use a center support. Use 2x3's for walls and for pitched-roof rafters, 2x4's for a flat roof.

For finishing outside walls you can use exterior plywood, Masonite, or exterior sheet materials such as Texture 1-11, Panelgroove, Ridgegroove, Shadowvent, etc. Roll, asphalt shingle, or any roofing used on a regular house can be used here, as well as Masonite, corrugated Fiberglas, corrugated aluminum, or corrugated cement-asbestos panels.

Windows. You can use stock storm sash for windows, or buy complete window units, such as those made by Andersen. Andersen windows come complete with frame and simplify construction, for they merely have to be nailed in the prepared opening. Always get your windows before preparing any opening and you won't have a wrong-sized opening.

Dutch door is good on any play house for it makes it easy to play store. On the walls which support rafters, the 2x4 upper plate is doubled, as shown. Roof sheathing is ¾-inch tongue-and-groove boards.

Tepee made of 3 panels of plywood cut into 6 pie-shaped sections. All joints hinged with canvas.

The stud walls of 2x4's are plumbed and braced. The pitched roof has 2x4 rafters, as shown here.

Tree houses. Few things can give a child, particularly a boy, so much pleasure as a tree house. Grownups often like them too, as a place to get away from it all. Basically, a tree house is a nest or aerie, and as such stirs the imagination. By climbing into it, the world is cut off, especially if a rope ladder or knotted rope is the only access and it is pulled up. A trap door can also be shut "to cut off enemies below."

The prime consideration in a tree house is safety. Avoid making it over 10 or 12 feet high. And build it strong enough to take a several hundred pound load. There's likely to be some jumping around up there.

You don't want to hurt your tree, or trees, so you may want to consult a tree surgeon about any drastic use of bolts or other fasteners. A 2-bole tree is one of the easiest in which to build. Two trees close together amount to about the same thing. Using 2x4 or 2x6 planks for your floor, you can safely cantilever (extend out) up to 4 feet from the support.

Building technique. The tree house of which construction is illustrated was designed by the celebrated architect, Eliot Noyes. He built it himself at his own home for his children. It demonstrates how a tree house can be a most handsome asset on your property.

The first step was to attach 2x8's to the tree trunks and level them. An extra 2x8 on one side allows for the tree's slant. Across the 2x8's, 2x4's were nailed for the floor, leaving a trap opening at one bole. Across the 2x8 ends and along outside edges, 2x4's were nailed. They serve as nailers for walls and also floor boards. The wall boards are spaced to allow peeking out. A 2x4 rail, attached to 4x4 corner posts, is the upper support for the walls.

Since the roof doesn't have to bear as much load as the floor, 2x6's are used as main supports, 2x4's along outer edges. The end 2x4's overhang a foot for design purposes. You can make a tree house roof any height you desire. A 5-foot ceiling is right

Window is completely preassembled and weatherstripped Andersen unit. Opening is prepared for it. The asphalt shingle roofing is applied to match that of grownup's house and first course is doubled.

Finish floor is Masonite over tongue-and-groove sheathing. Smooth Masonite easy to sweep clean.

This handsome tree house was designed and built by architect Eliot Noyes for his own children.

A pair of 2x6's spiked to twin trunks support a platform of spaced planks, safe, solid flooring.

The trapdoor gives access to the house, can be shut down to lock out "enemy" attack from below.

for most small fry. If they have to stoop, it may add to pleasure. A hole in the roof permits climbing up on the roof as well as further up the tree. No roofing was used. The ladder up to the house is made of 2x2's, with 1x2's set in dadoes as steps.

Wire supports. Where there are support problems, you may sometimes be able to solve them with guy wires. Use stranded, galvanized iron sash cord. A $\frac{3}{16}$-inch sash cord has a breaking strength of 688 pounds, costs about 6 cents per foot. A safe work load is $\frac{1}{5}$ the breaking strength.

You can attach wires to screweyes recessed in the tree's bark. You don't need turnbuckles. When fastening at the screweye, turn back six inches of wire. Unlay the wire and bind one strand at a time to form a taper.

Rope Ladder. To make a rope ladder for going up to the tree house, use 1- to 1¼-inch hardwood dowels a minimum of 15 inches long. Cut a notch on two sides for the rope, 1 inch in from the ends. Make the notch about ¾ inch wide. Its purpose is to hold the rope in place.

Space the rungs 14 inches apart, inserting them between spread strands of ¾-inch manila rope. At each rung, lash the rope on either side for 2 inches with 3-strand seine twine. Cost of ¾-inch manila is about 10 cents a foot. You may prefer using ½-inch nylon (24 cents per foot), or ⅝-inch polyethylene (28 cents) rope. All have about the same strength.

Tree house variations. You can put a tree house on stilts, so that it is completely independent of the tree for its support. It is

Ladder, made of 1x2's recessed in 2x2 uprights, spaced 16 inches apart, should be carefully made.

A tree house platform can be any shape. Making climb up into it a bit daring, above, adds fun.

Triangular tree house supported on 3-bole tree. Allow at least 1½-inch clearance around trunks.

Two of tree's boles form sides of ladder up to house. Rope is lowered for hoisting up supplies.

unlikely that you will want to make such a house very high. A ladder can serve as support on one end.

One interesting variation is a double-platform tree house. Use two trees, spaced some feet apart, with a bridge between the platforms on each tree. Platforms can be supported by legs made of 4x4's.

In constructing any tree house, allow 1½ inches clearance around the tree for future growth.

Use a swiveled pulley, attached to a screweye set in a branch, as a hoist for bringing supplies up to the tree house. The rope can be made fast to a cleat. A basket, box, or suitcase can be used as a receptacle.

The main tree house can be in the lower part of the tree. A second platform can be higher up. •

Floor joist arrangement in a 4-tree house. Tarp overhead serves as "tent" roof in rainy weather.

kid's playhouse

**It can double as storage
space in the wintertime**

YOUNGSTERS won't want to wander if they have this attractive house to play in; they'll keep themselves occupied for hours.

Amazingly sturdy, it is easy to knock down and move. With panels added to the window openings, it provides ample winter storage for garden tools, lawn furniture and bulky summer sports equipment.

Construction is simplified by the prefabricated panel sub-assemblies that make this playhouse so easy to erect.

Fabricate all sections completely with nails and waterproof glue before assembling. Framing members may be predrilled for the bolts and wing nuts before fabricating, or may be drilled with the completed panels erected to insure matching hole locations. Study the diagrams for details. •

PARTS SCHEDULE

CODE	NO. REQ'D	SIZE	PART IDENTIFICATION
A	1	¾"x43½"x81"	Floor
B	2	½"x48"x48"	Side
C	2	24"x29"	Front Panel
D	1	24"x84"	Rear Panel
E	2	22⅜"x29"	Rear Panel
F	2	7¼"x84"	Beam Support
G	1	¾"x25⅞"x23"	Door
H	2	¾"x48"x72"	Roof
J	2	13"x22⅜"	Louver Door
K	4	1⅝"x22⅜"	Casing
	32 Lin. Ft.	2"x4" Stock	Base and Beams
	122 Lin. Ft.	2"x2" Stock	Framing
	50 Lin. Ft.	½"x1" Stock	Stops
	30 Lin. Ft.	½"x2½" Stock	Louvers
	4 Ea.	For ½" Doors	Hinges
	2 Ea.	For ¾" Doors	Hinges
	40 Ea.	¼" Stove	Wing Nuts and Bolts
	2 Pcs.	22⅜"x25¼"	Clear Plastic Sheets*
	1 Pc.	6"x72"	Canvas Strip

Miscellaneous—8d Common and 6d Finish Nails (Galvanized)

*Optional

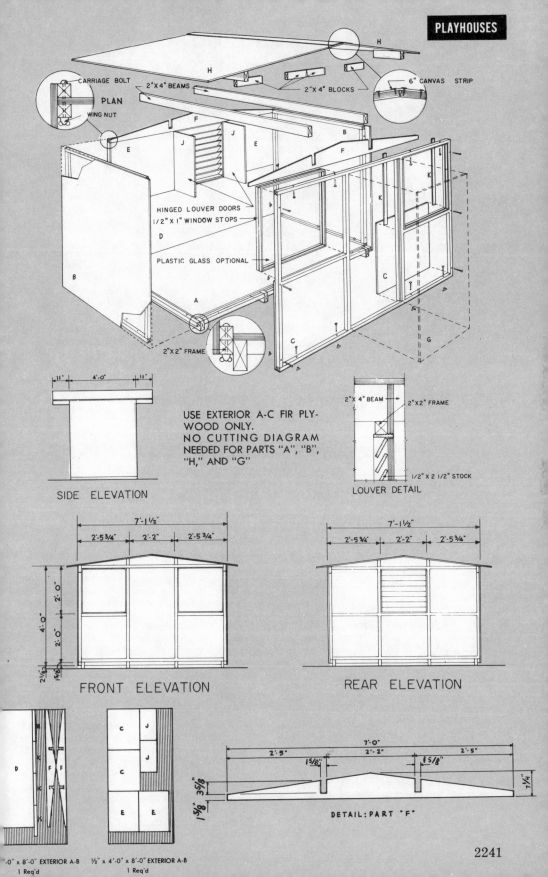

CARRIAGE BOLT

PLAN

WING NUT

2"X 4" BEAMS

2"X 4" BLOCKS

6" CANVAS STRIP

HINGED LOUVER DOORS

1/2" X 1" WINDOW STOPS

PLASTIC GLASS OPTIONAL

2"X 2" FRAME

SIDE ELEVATION

11"   4'-0"   11"

USE EXTERIOR A-C FIR PLY-
WOOD ONLY.
NO CUTTING DIAGRAM
NEEDED FOR PARTS "A", "B",
"H," AND "G"

2"X 4" BEAM   2"X2" FRAME

1/2" x 2 1/2" STOCK

LOUVER DETAIL

FRONT ELEVATION

7'-1½"
2'-5¾"   2'-2"   2'-5¾"
2'-0"
4'-0"
2'-0"
2½"

REAR ELEVATION

7'-1½"
2'-5¾"   2'-2"   2'-5¾"

DETAIL: PART "F"

7'-0"
2'-5"   2'-2"   2'-5"
1 5/8"   1 5/8"
3 5/8"
1 5/8"
7¼"

'-0" x 8'-0" EXTERIOR A-B
1 Req'd

½" x 4'-0" x 8'-0" EXTERIOR A-B
1 Req'd

2241

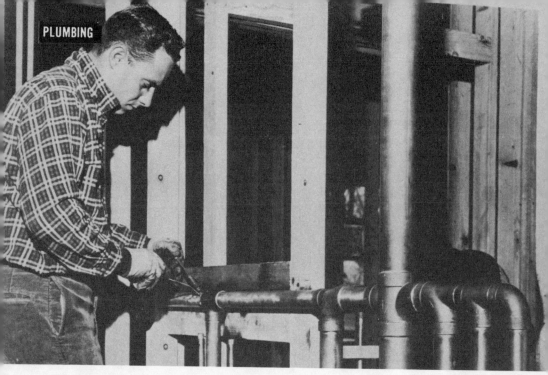

Chase Brass and Copper

Vents provide the air needed for free flow of sewage down the drains. Here several branch vent lines are connected to the stack. Stack is large, vertical drain and vent pipe extend up through the roof.

how plumbing works

...AND WHAT YOU SHOULD KNOW

A PLUMBING SYSTEM consists of two kinds of piping: one supplying water, the other carrying waste water and sewage away.

Water supply plumbing is very simple. It can be considered as an extended hose with many branches, leading the water wherever it is desired. Shutoffs and faucets control the water flow. Pipes can be small because the water is under pressure. Getting the pipes through walls, and wherever they are going, presents few problems because of this small size.

Water supply pipes which extend upward a story or more are known as risers. To prevent water-hammer, a banging in pipes caused when faucets are quickly turned off, vertical lengths of pipe are commonly installed near each faucet to serve as air-chamber shock absorbers.

Drainage pipes are large. They have to be because the relatively slow flow through them is by gravity. Because of the gravity flow, drainage pipes must have a continual pitch of at least ¼ inch per foot from the time they leave a fixture until

they reach the sewer. Even the fittings used in assembling drainage pipe have a built-in pitch.

Large vertical drain pipes are known as stacks. Horizontal drains are usually called waste pipes, or soil pipes if they carry toilet sewage. A stack that carries toilet waste is known as a soil stack.

The main drainage line from the house is known as the house drain. It continues 5 to 10 feet out through the foundation and after that point is known as the house sewer. The house sewer connects either to a septic tank, or to a public sewer in the street.

Vents. It is difficult to pour liquid out of a can that has just one hole punched in its top. Punch another hole for air, and the liquid flows freely. For the same reason, drain lines need air, and it is supplied by vent pipes. There must be a vent pipe near each fixture. A vent may continue on up through the roof and be open to the air, or several vents may connect onto a single large vent, or stack, which extends up through the roof to the air.

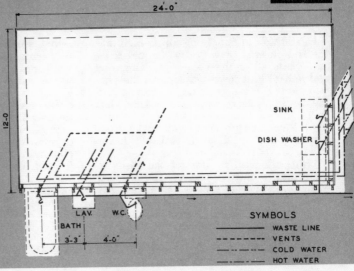

Installation plans for plumbing are usually shown in a schematic drawing like this. You may find it helpful to use these symbols in planning your plumbing project.

Chase Brass and Copper

Vent pipes (below) extend through to the open air above the roof and, where there is any danger of frost, should be at least 3 inches in diameter. Flashing is used to seal up the vent-roof joint.

Roughing-in is the installation of all plumbing except for fixtures. Pipe ends are capped until the wall finish is complete. Shown are the stack, branch vents, wastes, and water lines.

Dow Saraloy Flashing

Trap is the U-shaped pipe which holds water and seals off sewer gases from the house. Vents prevent waste from siphoning traps dry. To check if a trap is properly filled, open as shown here.

Cleanouts must be provided wherever the drain line makes a turn, or where any stoppages might occur. Brass cleanout plug here is installed where house drain exists through the foundation.

In addition to supplying air to facilitate the free flowing of waste water and sewage, vents allow the escape of dangerous and unhealthful sewer gases from the system. So that these gases do not escape into the house, it is of vital importance that every joint in the venting system be airtight. Vents also prevent waste water from coming back up through traps at lower levels.

Traps are used to seal off the gases in the drainage lines. A trap usually consists of a curved piece of pipe which always remains filled with water. Waste passes freely through the trap, but the water level remains undisturbed as a seal. Here again, the vents play a part. If a fixture drain were not properly vented, the rush of waste water from the fixture would create a vacuum and suck the trap dry. Such siphonage is a hazard to health, for it opens the sewer to the house.

In older houses, if water goes down the drain with a great sucking sound, it usually indicates the trap is being siphoned. In such cases, and where the installation of a vent to correct the condition would be extremely difficult, many codes permit the installation of a special "anti-siphon trap." It does the job of a standard vented trap. •

House drain becomes the house sewer at a point 5 to 10 feet beyond foundation line. Cast-iron drain pipe is being connected here to a fiber pipe, acceptable in some areas for sewer lines.

All vent and drainage lines must be pitched at least ¼ inch per foot. Here the house sewer line, connecting to septic tank, is being tested for pitch. The opening in foreground is a cleanout.

Septic tank is a watertight receptacle, typically of 750 or 1000 gallon capacity, in which sewage, by bacterial action, is converted into liquid and absorbed by soil.

PLUMBING TERMS

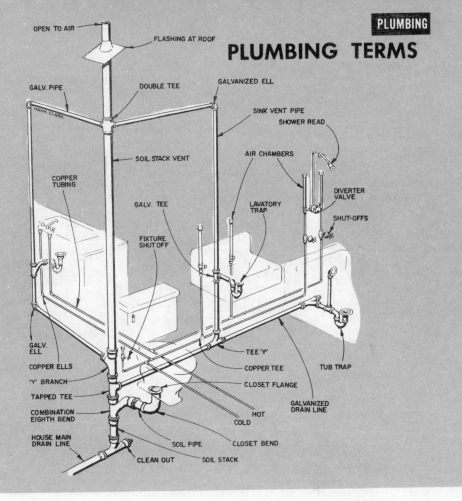

OPEN TO AIR
FLASHING AT ROOF
GALV. PIPE
DOUBLE TEE
GALVANIZED ELL
HANK CLARK
SINK VENT PIPE
SHOWER HEAD
SOIL STACK VENT
AIR CHAMBERS
COPPER TUBING
DIVERTER VALVE
GALV. TEE
LAVATORY TRAP
SHUT-OFFS
FIXTURE SHUT OFF
GALV. ELL
COPPER ELLS
TEE 'Y'
COPPER TEE
TUB TRAP
'Y' BRANCH
CLOSET FLANGE
TAPPED TEE
GALVANIZED DRAIN LINE
COMBINATION EIGHTH BEND
HOT
COLD
HOUSE MAIN DRAIN LINE
SOIL PIPE
CLOSET BEND
CLEAN OUT
SOIL STACK

Air chamber: A short length of vertical pipe, usually connected near a faucet, which serves to cushion the shock when water flow is abruptly stopped.

Branch: Any secondary water pipe or waste line which serves one fixture only.

Cleanout plug: An access opening for servicing clogged drain pipes.

Closet flange: A fitting for attaching a toilet to its drain pipe.

House drain: The main drainage pipe which conducts the discharge from all branch pipes to a point just outside the house foundation wall.

House sewer: The piping that continues from the end of the house drain and which connects to a septic tank or the public sewer in the street.

Main: A principal pipe to which branches are attached.

Plumbing: All pipes and fixtures for water supply and for both sanitary and storm drainage.

Riser: A water supply pipe which extends vertically at least one story.

Roughing in: Installation of the entire plumbing system except for fixtures. This includes installation of drainage, vents, water supply piping, and fixture supports.

Septic tank: A large water-tight receptacle which receives sewage from the drainage system and by bacterial action converts it to harmless liquid.

Soil pipe: A pipe carrying toilet sewage.

Stack: A main, vertical soil, waste, or vent pipe.

Trap: A curved pipe, holding water, which prevents the backpassage of gases from the drainage system, while allowing free flow of waste water or sewage through it.

Vent: A pipe supplying air to drainage lines.

Waste pipe: A pipe carrying other than toilet sewage.

Wet vent: A section of pipe serving for drainage as well as venting.

the right kind of pipe
... MAKES ALL THE DIFFERENCE

THERE ARE MANY kinds and qualities of pipe for water supply, drainage and vent lines. By understanding the strong and weak points of each type of piping, you'll be prepared to make the best selection for your own particular needs. An ideal pipe would cost less, be easier to install, and last longer than any other. Unfortunately, there is no one piping material which meets all these requirements. Local codes may also have some say about which varieties of pipe you can use.

Water Supply Pipes. Galvanized steel, copper, brass, plastic, and galvanized wrought iron pipe are commonly used for water supply systems. Black iron pipe is not used; it rusts too quickly. Lead pipe is not recommended, though it may be used for making a "gooseneck connection" between the water main in the street and the house service line.

● Galvanized steel pipe has the lowest initial cost of all types. Its usual life is from 15 to 30 years and in some areas gives what is considered satisfactory service. New York City code, for example, requires it. However, if it has to be replaced at any time, it's cost to you will be far higher than the most expensive kind of plumbing you can get.

Steel pipe is subject to deposits of salts and lime which gradually restrict water flow and which may eventually choke the flow off completely. It is corroded by both

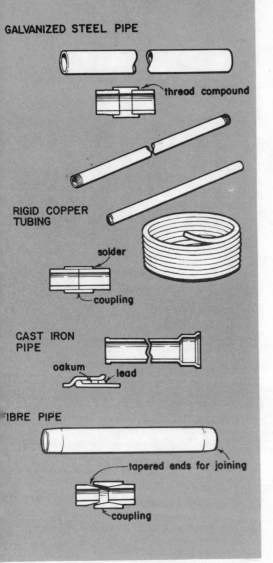

GALVANIZED STEEL PIPE

thread compound

RIGID COPPER TUBING

solder

coupling

CAST IRON PIPE

oakum   lead

FIBRE PIPE

tapered ends for joining

coupling

Tools required for roughing in copper plumbing in an entire house. For the large tank of gas, a small hand-torch can easily be substituted. Most are tools found in average home workshop.

Cast iron is most durable material for drainage, waste and vent lines, but assembly is slower. Shown here are the tools used in roughing in a typical all-ferrous home plumbing installation.

alkaline and acid waters. Carbonic acid in water attacks the zinc coating of the pipe, then the steel itself. Hot water is more acid than cold, and so these lines usually give out first.

Steel pipe comes in standard 21-foot lengths threaded at each end. Usually a pipe of ¾ to 1-inch diameter is big enough to supply all the water needed for both hot and cold water systems in a house. The ¾-inch size is adequate for main hot water or cold water lines and ½-inch pipe for branch lines to fixtures. Sizes of pipe always refer to internal diameters.

● Copper is the easiest to install of all water-line types, and is the first choice for either the professional or the nonprofes-

Copper tubing is unexcelled for both hot- and cold-water lines. It has such a smooth interior surface that it can be used one size smaller than galvanized steel pipe. Assembly is easy.

Because of its light weight, copper lends itself to "shop fabrication." Entire assemblies can be made wherever it is most convenient and then placed right into position in the house structure.

Copper & Brass Research Assoc.

sional installer. Copper will last as long as the house, and can meet the demands of areas where water is extremely corrosive. Its inside surface is much smoother than that of steel pipe, and one size smaller can be used without reduction of water flow. Where ¾-inch steel pipe is required, for example, ½-inch copper is more than satisfactory.

A ¾-inch copper line is usually enough to supply a house. A 1-inch size is used if there are flush valves on toilets, a lawn sprinkler system, a water-cooled air conditioner which discards water, or other heavy-demand equipment. For supply lines to toilet and basins, ⅜-inch tubing is commonly used, though some codes require ½, sometimes even ⅝-inch size. Supply to bathtubs is usually ½ inch.

Copper tubing costs a little more than steel pipe, but its fittings cost less and if you are paying for installation labor, your bill should be about 25 per cent less. Copper tubing is usually assembled by means of sweat (soldered) fittings, occasionally by flare or compression fittings. Sweat joints are easier to make than threaded joints, and they are stronger. Threading pipe thins it down, weakens it.

Copper tubing is made in three wall thicknesses: K, L, and M. Type K is the heaviest and is used underground. Type L is somewhat lighter and is used for in-terior plumbing and for radiant heating installation. Type M is lightest and is designed especially for radiant heating.

Both Type K and Type L tubing are available either in rigid (hard temper), or flexible (soft temper) varieties. Rigid tubing is usually offered in 20-foot lengths, though Sears offers it in 10. Flexible K type is produced in 60 and 100-foot coils, but you may be able to buy part of a coil. Type L is also available in 30-foot coils.

Flexible tubing is best for running up through existing walls in remodeling jobs, or when replacing clogged or rusted out galvanized pipe. It's also better for ground burial, for it can be readily bent around rocks and other obstructions. It will take some freezing without being appreciably damaged and will give a little, rather than burst, as earth settles.

Because of its flexibility, soft temper tubing requires fewer fittings, and it is best for vertical lines where some bending is often necessary. However, hard temper tubing, with solder fittings, makes the neatest installations and is required for horizontal lines. Flexible tubing, used horizontally, is likely to sag, creating pockets which make drainage difficult. Solder fittings can be used with either flexible or rigid tubing, but flared or compression fittings are designed for flexible tubing only.

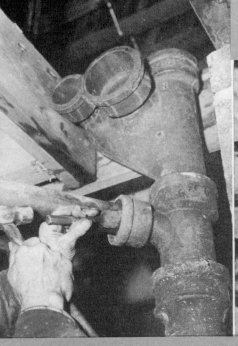

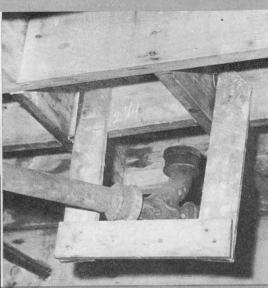

-iron drainage is heavy, has many joints, is so bulky that thicker walls are required ccommodate it. Cost of the material, however, auch less than the cost for copper tubing.

Because cast iron is so heavy, it often may require special, sturdy support. A completed installation is never so neat-looking or as compact as copper. But it's much more durable.

● Brass pipe is the most expensive of types. Originally it was used as yellow ss, composed of 60 per cent copper and st of the rest zinc. Then it was found that brass with an 80 per cent copper con-t was more durable. The feeling today is t for most water purposes straight cop- is superior, and brass is now commonly d only for exposed water supply lines ich are chrome plated.

Like copper, brass water pipe has very ooth inside surfaces and can be used size smaller than steel or iron pipe. It oined with threaded fittings. Brass has ut the same wall thickness as steel pipe comparable size, and threads are the ne.

● Wrought iron. Cost is high, use lim- l. It's a durable pipe, resistant to certain rosive waters. It is not to be confused h steel pipe.

● Plastic pipe is tough, lightweight, y to cut, handle, join, and is inexpensive. s unexcelled for cold water lines, but as cannot be recommended for general with hot water for it won't take tem- atures above 160 degrees.

Plastic is the number one choice for well es, water sprinkling systems, swimming ol plumbing, running a line for a hose k, for connecting to a water softener, or y other cold water use, codes permitting. is not harmed by occasional freezing,

Even though you make other drainage, waste and vent lines of copper, you will still have to switch to cast iron for any underground piping, and for section where main drain leaves house.

For vent section of stack, you can save money in material cost and in labor by switching from cast-iron pipe to Transite pipe. This cement-asbestos pipe is joined by standard caulking.

Copper is available in both hard temper and flexible varieties. The flexible kind is easily bent and shaped by the hands alone, but hard temper copper can be bent only by means of a special tool.

won't rust, corrode, or rot. The Orangeburg Company, one of the largest producers of plastic pipe, guarantees their product unconditionally for twenty years, and will even pay labor costs if replacement should be necessary during that period. Tests indicate plastic pipe will easily last in excess of thirty years.

Plastic pipe comes in several types. Polyethylene pipe is the lightest pipe of all, is joined by means of slip fittings and stainless steel clamps. A vinyl type (PVC, or polyvinyl chloride), is commonly joined by solvent cementing of slip fittings, may also be threaded or welded. Plastic pipe is readily available in sizes from ½ to 2 inches. One hundred feet of the ½-inch size weighs 7 pounds, costs $8, as compared with 30 pounds and $30 for copper, and 100 pounds and $15 for steel. It comes in long lengths (up to 3500 feet in some cases), requires fewer fittings.

Drainage and Venting Pipe. Types commonly used are cast iron, threaded steel, copper, plastic, lead, bituminized fiber, asbestos cement, and vitrified clay.

● Cast iron, almost without exception, is the choice for the underground, main drainage line that extends from the base of the soil stack, through the house foundation wall and from 5 to 10 feet beyond. It has no superior for use as the line running from that point to the septic tank or public sewer in the street. Cast iron is also frequently used for the soil stack (the main vent and drainage line which extends up through the roof), and for branch drainage and vent lines connecting to it. Sometimes, however, for reasons of economy, these branches are made of steel.

Cast iron is very durable and long lasting. It is generally accepted that it will last the life of the house. It is also expensive, heavy, and time-consuming to assemble. Because of its weight, it needs strong support. Because of its bulk, it requires a 2x6 stud wall instead of a standard 2x4 one.

Cast-iron pipe comes in 5-foot lengths and commonly in 2-, 3-, and 4-inch (nominal) inside diameter for homes. One end of each pipe length terminates in a hub or bell, into which the straight spigot of the following section fits. This joint is sealed with a rope-like packing, called oakum, and lead. The lead is usually poured in when molten, but lead wool, which is

Cascade Pools

Plastic pipe is low in cost, light in weight, flexible, extremely durable, and easy to cut and assemble. It comes in coils and also in unbroken lengths of hundreds of feet. Plastic is not as yet suitable for hot water lines, but it has proven to be unexcelled for wells, sprinkling systems, swimming pools, and other cold-water uses.

pounded in cold, may be permitted in some cases.

Cast-iron pipe comes in service weight, and "standard" or "extra heavy weight." Save by using service weight when codes permit. Because of a new spin method of manufacture, service weight pipe is as durable as the standard pipe was formerly

Lengths of cast-iron pipe are available with a hub at each end. These are handy for cutting short lengths of pipe, since two short sections can be made from one pipe, each piece having a hub end.

● Steel pipe can be used for the main stack and vent lines, but it cannot be used underground. It's far lighter than cast iron, an important consideration in remodeling jobs, particularly in an old house whose structure may not be able to take an excessive amount of added weight. For drainage and vent purposes, steel pipe comes in diameters from 1¼ to 4 inches. It is easily assembled with a chain wrench. Special threaded cast-iron drainage fittings are used with steel pipe. It is not the longest lasting pipe by far, but it is low cost and can offer adequate service particularly in remodeling an older house.

● Copper is made in type M for drainage and in a special economical DWV weight (drainage, waste, vent), permitted by codes in many areas for above ground use. Type M, being heavier, has generally satisfactory durability. It is, however, considerably more expensive than cast iron. Type DWV, thinner walled, is not so durable as type M, but under normal use can be expected to give many years of service.

Either type is light in weight (only about ¼ as much as cast iron), and certainly the easiest type of drainage system to install. A special fitting connects it to the cast-iron underground house drain. The 20-foot lengths in which the copper tubing comes means fewer joints. Assembly is quick and easy with solder-joint drainage fittings. These special fittings are made with a built-in pitch of ¼ inch per foot. The smooth interior of copper tubing and lack of shoulders at joints means faster drainage and less likelihood of clogging.

● Bituminous fiber pipe, such as Orangeburg, is used for house sewers and in septic tank installations. It is lowest in cost of all types, light in weight, comes in 5-foot lengths so that few joints are re-

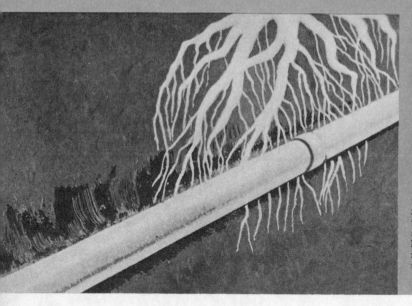

Roots can be destructive to house sewers. If joints aren't tight, roots may enter and clog the line. The fewer the joints, and the more permanent they are, the less trouble for you.

Johns-Manville

Bituminized fiber pipe is most economical kind for sewer and septic tank disposal lines. Assembly is simply made by snap couplings. At right—perforated type used in drain fields.

Orangeburg Mfg. Co.

quired as compared with clay pipe. Joints are made simply by tapping on fittings, are so tight root penetration is seldom a problem. Cutting can be done with an ordinary carpenter's handsaw.

The pipe, impregnated with coal tar pitch, is rotproof and noncorrosive, but excessively hot water and some chemicals may soften it. Because it is slightly flexible, it can take soil movement without cracking or pulling out at the joints. On the other hand, unless its bed is properly made, and backfilling done exactly as directed, it is subject to crushing or collapsing. Codes may require you to come at least ten feet out from your foundation with cast-iron pipe. After that, you can save by switching to a bituminous fiber pipe. An adapter connects it to the spigot end of cast-iron pipe.

● Vitrified clay pipe is often used for building drains which run underground. It doesn't corrode or wear, and if it isn't subject to stresses which crack or break it, it will last indefinitely. For home sewer lines, 4-foot sections are the popular choice, but other lengths are available. Each section has a bell at one end for joining to the plain end of the next pipe section. Joints are made by packing in oakum to a depth of about ½ inch, then sealing with an asphalt joining compound. The oakum is necessary to keep the compound from getting inside the pipe.

Drawbacks are its many joints, and the possible invasion of them by tree roots if joints are defective, also the increased labor in laying it as compared with the longer-length lighter-weight piping. Most joint trouble with clay pipe in the past was because mortar was used for jointing it. Stick with asphalt, either hot or cold, and you aren't likely to encounter trouble.

● Other types. Asbestos-cement pipe is used for sewer and vent lines, comes in five and ten-foot lengths, can be cut with a carpenter's handsaw. It has the advantage of fewer joints and light weight.

Concrete pipe is similar to vitrified clay pipe in its use and assembly, but it is not as durable.

Plastic pipe promises to come into widespread use shortly for both drainage and vent lines. Plastic is light in weight, noncorroding, easily assembled. All that is holding it back at present is code acceptance and price. ●

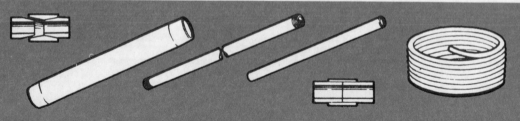

Brass has been largely displaced by copper for home plumbing systems. It's still used, however, for chrome-plated exposed piping, such as that found in water supply lines and lavatory traps.

Chase Brass & Copper Co.

Lead is not recommended for water lines, but has limited uses elsewhere. One of its few applications is for "closet bends," the section of pipe joining the toilet to the soil line. The right kind of pipe, you'll find, does make a difference.

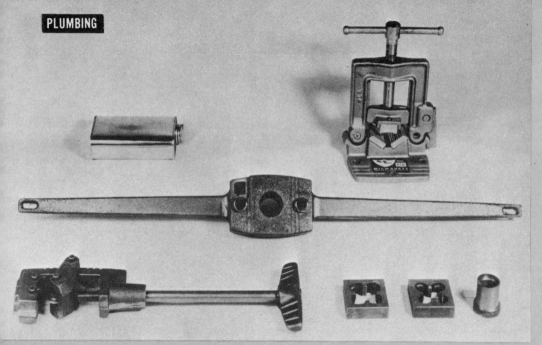

Milwaukee Tool & Equipment Co.

A kit of tools for cutting, threading and working steel pipe can be bought for about $30, and is a worthwhile addition to any workshop. It will cut pipe to 2 inches, thread ½- and ¾-inch pipe.

plumbing tools

. . . AND HOW TO USE THEM

OFTEN, HALF THE JOB is having the right tool for it. Watching a plumber at work, it's apparent how large a role his tools play in his work and how simple they make otherwise difficult jobs. It is wasteful of effort, and sometimes dangerous, to try to undertake a job with makeshift tools.

Many of the tools needed in plumbing are ones that can have continuing use around the house, and are worthwhile additions to any workshop collection. A good pair of pipe wrenches, such as those made by Ridgid, will be of regular use to you. You're also likely to find enough continuing use for pipe cutting and threading tools to justify acquiring a set. Most economically, they can be bought in kit form. One, manufactured by the Milwaukee Tool & Equipment Company of Milwaukee 46, Wisconsin, includes a pipe vise, a threader for ½- and ¾-inch pipe, a cutter for pipe up to 2 inches, plus a can of cutting oil. It sells for just over $30.

Other tools, which are specialized and rarely needed, can be borrowed or rented. Sears, Roebuck stores lend light or heavy tools free for installing plumbing when you buy your plumbing materials from them.

Pipe Vises. A vise with toothed jaws is needed for working with iron or brass pipe, but not for copper. You can't hold pipe steady enough for cutting or threading in a mechanic's vise. If you have a standard mechanic's vise, you may, however, be able to buy serrated pipe jaws to adapt it for plumbing use. If you plan to buy an all-purpose vise, get one that is a combination pipe and mechanic's vise, and it will serve for your occasional plumbing jobs.

For limited use, it is possible to improvise a pipe holding tool with a pipe wrench. The wrench is set between cleats and the pipe is slipped through a U-bolt or large staple. Or you can use a mechanic's vise, in combination with a pipe wrench, for the purpose. The vise is tightened just enough to hold the pipe firmly. The wrench takes the real grip which keeps the pipe from turning.

A good pipe vise, with up to 2-inch capacity, costs about $15, but you can buy a satisfactory vise with a capacity to 2½ inches for only $10. A small vise, with a capacity to 1¼ inches sells for $5 up. Some

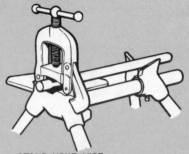

STAND YOKE VISE

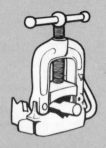

BENCH YOKE VISE

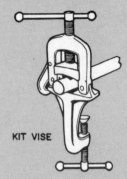

KIT VISE

The most popular vise types include stand yoke, bench yoke, and post chain vises. Note the differences as is shown here. Also pipe jaws can often be added to ordinary mechanic's vise, adapting it for plumbing use, doubling the ordinary duty.

Milwaukee Tool & Equipment Co.

POST CHAIN VISE

PIPE JAWS

Bench vise is bolted to workbench flush with the front edge. Position vise so even long lengths of pipe can be held in its jaws. Release on vise side permits rapid freeing of held pipe.

Pipe must be held firmly for cutting. Place a cutter wheel on line of desired cut, advance it by turning handle slightly each time the cutter is revolved. While working, use cutting oil.

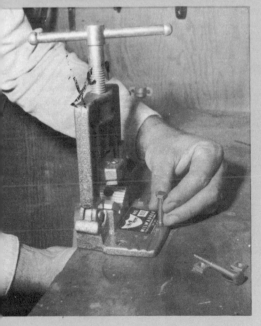

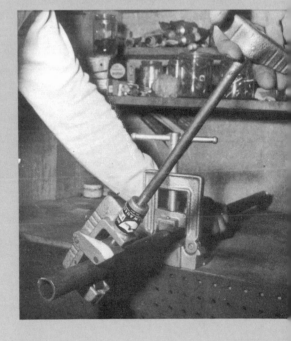

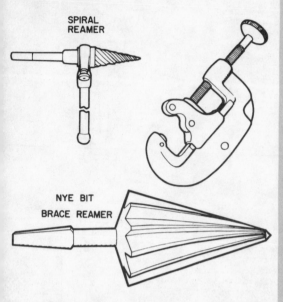

SPIRAL
REAMER

NYE BIT
BRACE REAMER

Simplest reamer has tapered shank to fit any standard brace-and-bit. Spiral ratchet reamer is used by professional plumbers. Tubing cutter has reamer which folds away, protects pockets.

vises have pipe rests and benders on their base.

Vises are hinged, so that by releasing a catch, the pipe is easily removed sideways. Pipe jaws are replaceable; some are reversible. In large vises, rods and pipes under $\frac{3}{8}$ inch are held securely at either side of the vise jaws. A long-jaw design, as in the Milwaukee vise, holds the pipe securely without damaging it, for the pressure is divided over the whole length of the holding jaws.

Some vises are designed to bolt to a bench, others clamp to it or are easily portable and attach to any bench or plank. A "post vise" can be attached by a chain to a lally column or other post.

Another type of pipe vise has a link chain, and is known as a chain vise. Pipe is held between a jaw and the chain. A chain vise usually has a down-under handle for tightening, but one new Ridgid model has a convenient top screw. The chain vise is a somewhat more compact tool than the standard pipe vise, and the price is likely to be lower. You can get one with up to 2-inch capacity for only $6. They are available with pipe rest and pipe benders.

Pipe and Tubing Cutters. These tools cut faster and better than a hack saw. It takes an expert to get a free-hand square cut with a hack saw, but a cutter gives a square cut every time, and a square cut is essential in getting a threading tool started right, and making flare joints.

Technique of use is simple. Loosen the cutting wheel by turning the handle until the tool can be slid on the pipe. Tighten the wheel on the cutting mark until it begins to bite into the pipe. The handle is turned a little every time the tool is revolved around pipe or tubing. This tightening of the

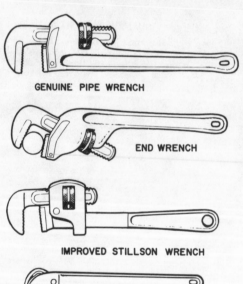

GENUINE PIPE WRENCH

END WRENCH

IMPROVED STILLSON WRENCH

STRAP WRENCH

Wrenches for working with pipe and plumbing fittings include heavy-duty, end, Stillson, strap, compound leverage, chain, spud, and hex wrenches. The new hex wrench will give a four-sided grip.

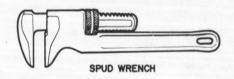

SPUD WRENCH

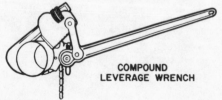

COMPOUND
LEVERAGE WRENCH

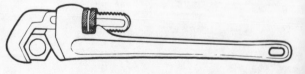

Heavy-duty pipe wrench is most important item in a plumbing kit. Two are needed: one to hold the pipe while other turns on fitting. The 18-inch model shown will handle pipes up to 2 inches.

handle keeps advancing the cutter wheel, until it finally comes all the way through. In cutting pipe, apply thread-cutting oil to the cutter wheel and the pipe as you work.

You can buy a "Saunders-type" cutter with capacity to one inch for about $6, to two inch for $9, a better one for $13.50. Most have a minimum capacity of ⅛ inch. Cutting wheels are usually replaceable for a dollar or two.

A standard type cutter has two rollers and one cutter, but you can also get models that have several cutting wheels. A 4-wheel cutter is designed for work in close quarters where it isn't possible to turn the tool completely around the pipe.

Tubing cutters cut copper, brass, and aluminum. One with 1-inch capacity can be bought for about $2, 1½ for about $3.50.

Reamers. A reamer is needed to remove internal burrs in pipe or tubing after cutting. Burrs will slow the flow of water or waste, may eventually cause clogging. Tubing cutters often have fold-in or retractable reamers attached.

Pipe reamers for use in a bit brace, for pipe to 1¼ inches, can be bought for about $2.50. These have spiral flutes and a tapered square shank. For pipe to 2 inches, prices begin at about $4.50. Plumbers use reamers with a ratchet handle. They are very convenient, but cost from $15 up.

If you don't have a reamer, you can use a file instead.

Wrenches. It is important to use the right wrench for the job at hand. Otherwise you can damage the pipe or fitting, the tool itself, or bruise your knuckles.

Stillson, pipe, chain, or strap wrenches are used for turning pipe or other round

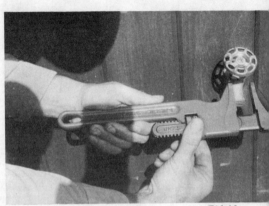

Spud wrench is handy utility monkey wrench, useful in gripping square or hexagon nuts and other flat-sided plumbing parts. Always adjust the wrench so its jaws fit snugly and fully on work.

Chain wrench is ideal for hard to get at spots. Needs less than ⅝-inch clearance to get at the work. Where handle swing is limited, the ratchet action allows new bite without removing the tool.

End pattern pipe wrench makes work easier when pipe is close to wall, or quarters are cramped. The offset is its only difference. Its operation is the same as any straight pipe wrench.

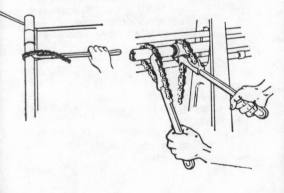

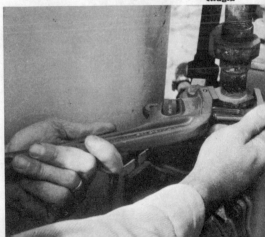

SQUEEZE TO LOCK ONTO WORK | PRESS HERE TO RELEASE!

Vise-Grip wrench can be used as an adjustable end wrench, pipe wrench, locking wrench, pliers, clamp, or portable vise. A squeeze wrench locks jaws on work, frees both hands to do many other things.

Self-gripping pliers have many plumbing uses. A toothed-jaw model serves as combination plier and wrench for places you can't reach with a pipe wrench. Smooth-jaw pliers are for plated fittings.

Channellock

stock. They should not be used on nuts or other flat-sided parts, for they will chew off the corners and will make it so the part can no longer be turned easily. A large pipe wrench, however, can safely be used on nuts that are an inch or more across without danger of damaging them.

Stillson-pattern wrenches are normally considered as "normal duty" pipe wrenches as compared with heavy-duty pipe wrenches. Two pipe wrenches are usually required. One holds the pipe while the other turns on the fitting. A 10- and an 18-inch wrench are usually best for average jobs, but some prefer 10- and 14-inch sizes. Actually, 10-inch wrench is designed for pipe to 1-inch, and 18-inch for pipe to 2 inches. The 14-incher handles 1½-inch pipe nicely.

The size of a pipe wrench is figured by the total length of the tool, plus a nominal extension of the jaws. A 14-inch wrench is thus the tool with its jaws open 1½

inches, an 18-inch, with the jaws open 2 inches.

Always turn a pipe wrench handle in the direction of its open jaws. That makes the jaws tighter. Don't abuse a wrench by twisting it sideways. It may get the jaws out of alignment.

Don't use a pipe or other toothed wrench on chrome pipe, or pipe you don't want marred, without taping the pipe so the teeth can't bite through. The preferred tool to use in such cases is a strap wrench or girth wrench.

To avoid bruised knuckles, pull a wrench instead of pushing it. If you must push, use the palm of your hand. It will protect the knuckles. A length of pipe over the wrench handle will give you extra leverage, but the wrench was not designed for that much extra stress, and may not take it. Also remember that the wrench gets tighter as you turn it, and may crush a pipe.

A good tool to use instead of a pipe

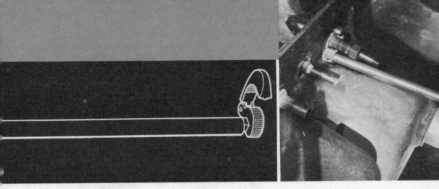

Basin wrench is designed for getting at nuts in close quarters and hard to reach spots, such as basin nuts, traps, flush valves, and ball cocks. Jaw is reversible, so that it can tighten or loosen.

Adjustable wrenches are versatile tools, but are only for light duty work. Always turn the wrench handle in the direction of its open jaws, never turn it the other way. Also don't twist sideways.

Sears, Roebuck

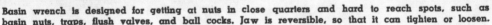

TURN WITH THE WRENCH

wrench on smaller sizes is a pair of locking pliers such as Vise-Grip. You can get a Vise-Grip into a corner where it is impossible to use a pipe wrench. For doing a job, like connecting a gas stove, a man with a Vise-Grip can beat one with a pipe wrench every time. You can buy a 10-inch Vise-Grip at your hardware store for under $3.

On faucets, valves, and other equipment, with flat-sided parts, use a spud (monkey) wrench, open end or adjustable wrench, or a pair of smooth-jawed Channel-lock pliers. For added protection of plated fittings and surfaces, tape them or use a strip of cardboard. On adjustable wrenches, put pressure on the stationary jaw only. Turn it only in the direction the wrench was designed to turn. The lower, adjustable jaw should always point in the direction of wrench movement, should never be pulling away from it. An adjustable wrench is not made for heavy use, and you are likely to break it if you exert heavy pressure, especially if its jaws are wide.

Open end or adjustable wrenches should fit snugly on the work. If they don't, they'll slip and round off the corners of the nut or fitting you're turning. Working in close corners, where you can't turn a nut or fitting far enough so that your open end wrench will fit on the next pair of flat sides, turn the wrench over and you'll find you can get a fit.

A ratcheting chain wrench is for use where a pipe wrench can't get. The chain needs only ½-inch clearance, and when you have parallel pipe lines which are very close together, or when a pipe is against a wall or in some other hard-to-get-at spot, it provides the answer. The ratcheting ac-

tion gives a new bite quickly, and without removing the wrench from the work. It is a time and effort saver where hand-swing is limited. The chain wrench will fit any shape bar, as well as to pipe and conduit.

A plier wrench, such as the Channel lock, gives strong gripping power in tight places that can't be reached by a pipe wrench. An interlocking principle prevents slipping under any load, since the heavier the job, the greater the interlocking action. Smooth-jawed Channel-lock pliers open to two inches for gripping sink trap nuts. The smooth jaws don't harm plated fittings.

A basin wrench is for tightening nuts in close and hard-to-reach places. These include basin nuts, traps, flush valves, etc.

End pipe wrenches are designed for use when pipe is close to a wall, or quarters are otherwise close. Aside from having the end pattern, it is like standard pipe wrenches.

You can usually get replacement parts for any pipe wrench made by a reputable manufacturer. Parts include handle, hook jaw, heel jaw, springs, nut and pin.

Threading Tools. A tool for threading pipe consists of a stock, which may be one- or two-handled, and a die and guide bushing or ring for each size pipe to be threaded. The die fits in the head of the stock along with a guide bushing. In some cases, the stock itself may be a guide for one pipe size. Some stocks have three die holders. These three-way threaders can thus thread three common sizes of pipe with no change-over required.

In setting up a threader, the guide bushing goes on the pipe first, serves to align the pipe and the die. The die fits in a receptacle on the other side of the stock. Each

3-WAY PIPE THREADER

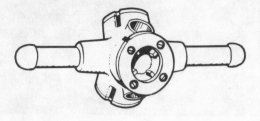

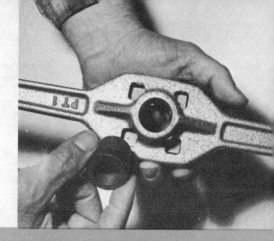

A three-way pipe threader has a stock accommodating three die-holders, and can thread three common sizes of pipe with no time or effort lost in making a changeover. It is a professional tool.

Threading tool has a guide bushing for each size of pipe to be threaded. The bushing fits into the stock. In the popular Milwaukee threader, the stock itself is a guide for one pipe size.

All threading photos courtesy of Milwaukee Tool & Equipment Co.

Die fits into receptacle on other side of stock from bushing. Face of the die is marked for the size of pipe for which it is to be used. Cover fits over die, is tightened by thumb screws.

In starting thread, stock is turned clockwise on pipe end until the die takes hold. The stock is then turned half a turn forward, back a quarter turn, until the cutting of thread is completed.

Before and during cutting of thread, cutting oil must be liberally applied to the die and the threads. The oil lubricates and cools the die, prolongs its life by preventing loss of temper.

Thread is cut until pipe's end projects half a turn beyond the end of the die. Threader is then removed by turning it counterclockwise. Wipe away surplus oil, chips, and job is done.

Round, file-type Surform is a handy tool for smoothing and enlarging pipe holes through floors, walls, and ceilings. It can cut through plaster, wood and masonry with almost the same easy facility.

Stanley Electric Tools

When roughing in pipes, saber saw is just the thing for cutting open floors and walls, notching studs and joists. Here saber saw is starting cut-out for countertop installation of the sink

Plumb and slope of pipes are frequently important. Also a good, accurate level is an essential tool. A Magnetic torpedo level will cling tightly to ferrous pipe, leaving hands free for other tasks.

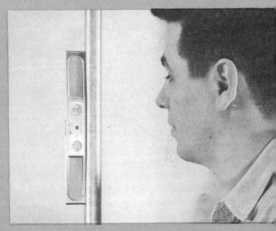

die is marked with the size of pipe for which it is used. Typically, the die is placed so that the lettering on it faces up toward the cover plate on the stock. The larger diameter of die threads are faced toward the guide bushing. The die cuts a tapered thread.

The threader should be oiled with cutting oil before starting the thread, and oiled liberally all during the threading process, usually every two or three turns. The oil lubricates and cools the die and prolongs its life by preventing loss of its temper. In starting the thread, turn the stock clockwise until the die takes hold. Turn the stock forward half a turn, then back a

quarter turn to break the chips. Continue until the pipe's end projects half a turn beyond the small end of the die. Remove the threader by turning it counterclockwise. Wipe away all surplus oil and chips, and the pipe is ready to use.

You can't cut good threads with a die that is worn, damaged, or clogged with chips, or if you skimp on oil while threading.

A threader with ratcheting action is especially helpful when working on pipe in close quarters.

Pipe taps are used for cutting internal threads. Some taps are offered in combination with drills which cut holes of exactly

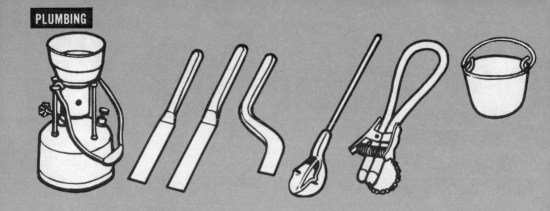

Tools used in working with cast-iron pipe include a gasoline furnace, offset yarning iron, caulking irons, cast-iron lead-melting pot with a pouring ladle, and an asbestos joint runner for protection.

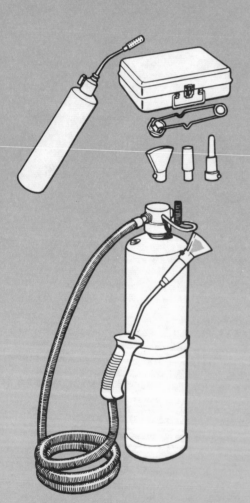

the right size for threading by the tap. Taps are marked with nominal pipe size and the number of threads per inch. The following table shows the drill size required for each size tap.

Tap	Drill	Threads per inch
1/8	21/64	27
1/4	29/64	18
3/8	19/32	18
1/2	21/32	14
3/4	15/16	14
1	1-3/16	11-1/2

Torches and Furnaces. A propane torch is far easier to use and much more convenient than a gasoline blow torch. The

Sears, Roebuck

Propane torches are available in inexpensive kits that come complete. New, handy type for plumbing has tank which clips on belt, and an extension hose. It is far less tiring and easier to handle.

Gasoline blow torches are more complicated to operate than propane ones. The better gasoline torches feature seamless, solid brass tanks, 2200° flame. Lower-priced models are of steel.

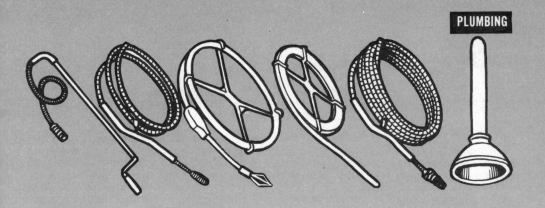

Tools for cleaning out clogged drain lines include closet auger, hood-end cleanout auger, flat sewer rod, flat, spring-steel auger, drain and trap auger, and a rubber force cup, sketched above.

handy disposable cylinders which contain its fuel are available everywhere, cost under $1.50. A torch is needed for making solder joints on copper tubing, for loosening frozen plugs, thawing pipes. It can also be used, if necessary, instead of a furnace for melting lead. Propane burns at 2300 degrees.

Torches are dangerous, especially when working in close quarters. Plumbers keep a water hose handy, just in case they start a fire. Use a piece of asbestos board or a doubled sheet of asbestos as a guard. Some wall insulation is inflammable, and if a wall has no fire-stop, a draft inside the wall may carry sparks upward and start a fire where you can't reach it unless you tear the wall open.

For a gasoline blowtorch, use only white unleaded gas. Fill the tank half-full, screw its plug tight. Pump the torch to build up air pressure. Then, holding one hand over the torch nozzle, open the needle valve, and let gas drip in the priming cup. When the cup is half full, turn off the valve, mop any spilled gas, and light the cup.

The flame serves to heat the vaporizing chamber. Just before the flame goes out, open the needle valve slowly to ignite the torch. If fire streams out, the vaporizing chamber isn't hot enough, and you'll have to start over.

When the torch is burning properly, pump occasionally to keep up air pressure. When shutting the torch off, avoid closing the valve too tightly. It will contract as it cools, and may freeze the needle in its seat.

A plumber's gasoline furnace is used for melting lead. Essentially, it works like a blowtorch. If the quantity of lead to be melted isn't large, you can apply a propane torch flame to a ladle to do the job. Further

details on melting lead, for caulking joints in cast-iron pipe, are given in another chapter.

Other tools used in caulking joints are a yarning iron for packing oakum in the joint, caulking irons for packing in lead, and an asbestos joint runner with spring clamp for pouring joints in horizontal pipe. Another type of joint runner employs rubber instead of asbestos.

Test Plugs. These are used to seal toilets and the open end of soil pipes when the stack and drainage system is being tested for leaks. In the test, the stack is filled from the roof with water. The plug itself may have a filler pipe or a cock. Turning a large wing nut expands the rubber plug, sealing the pipe or toilet opening.

Clogged-Drain Tools. A rubber force cup at the end of a stick, known popularly as "plumber's friend," dislodges obstructions in drains by means of air pressure. A force pump does a similar job, but develops more pressure. It has a plunger which is worked up and down.

A special auger, consisting of a flexible coil of spring steel with a crank at one end for rotating it, is used for cleaning toilets. Large augers or snakes, either worked by hand or power operated, may have special points, root cutter devices, or brushes to clean sewer and soil pipes. Sewer rods, with revolving spear points, come in lengths to 100 feet. When you call on professional help to do a job, this is the type of equipment they may have. One type may be powered by either a ¼-inch or a ½-inch electric drill.

Valve Seat Dresser. If replacement of a washer doesn't stop the drip, the seat is likely to be rough and require refinishing. The simple tool used costs under $1. •

copper tubing

... AND HOW TO WORK WITH IT

COPPER TUBING is the easiest kind of piping to install. You can use it for drains, vents, and water supply lines when adding an extra bath or powder room, for a new sink in the playroom or darkroom, or for adding sill cocks at convenient spots outdoors.

You can use it to replace rusted out or choked-up sections of galvanized piping. Special adapters make the connection from one kind of pipe to the other. You can use copper for extending heating lines, or replacing old-style standup radiators with space-saving, inconspicuous and more efficient baseboard units. It's just the thing for hooking up a new water heater or water softener. Almost no special tools are required in working with copper—no heavy wrenches or vises, no threading equipment.

In figuring the length of tubing needed for a connection, measure from the end of one fitting to the start of the next one; then add on the depth of the tubing which goes into each fitting.

Copper is quickly and easily assembled by "sweating" joints. The tubing in its fitting is heated until the solder touched to tubing melts. When the solder fills the joint, the job's done.

Chase Brass & Copper Co.

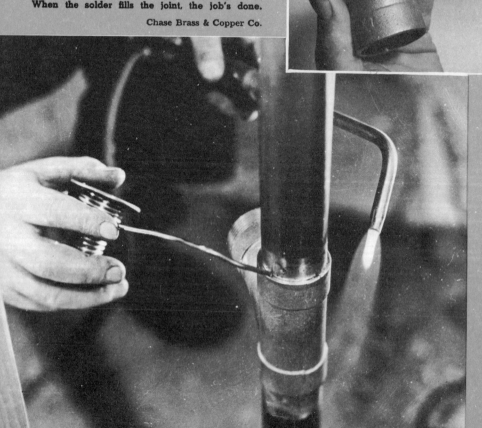

Types and Sizes. Copper tubing is available in heavy-duty type K and lighter type L. The latter is satisfactory for almost any above-ground home water line use, code permitting. Use type K underground. Either type can be had in flexible or rigid temper.

Use the flexible for vertical lines or for snaking through existing structures or close quarters. Use it underground. It will withstand some freezing, can be routed around obstructions, isn't bothered by minor earth movements. Flexible tubing is easily bent, making measurements for length less critical, and the necessity for joints fewer. It also comes in longer lengths. Rigid tubing comes in 20 footers,

maximum. Of course, in a single installation you may have to use both rigid and flexible types, employing each where it suits to best advantage.

You can use one size smaller copper tubing than galvanized pipe and get an equivalent water flow. Since a typical iron water pipe is ¾ inch, the typical copper one is ½. Fixture supply lines to toilet and lavatory may be only ⅜ inch. Sizes are ID (inside diameters). Small copper tubing, such as is used for oil lines, is usually sized OD (outside diameter). Main supply lines for the entire house are usually no more than ¾ inch. In sizing hot water lines, be especially careful not to oversize them. The smaller pipes have less heat loss, and

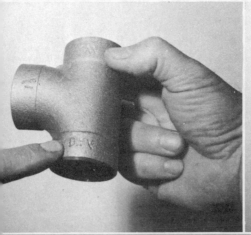

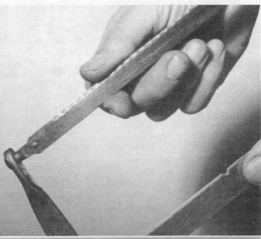

Special fittings are used for copper drainage lines. The lightest weight, lowest-cost fittings are Type DWV. Examine the fitting closely and you will be able to find identifying marking on it.

Tubing may be cut with a hack saw. Use a blade with 24 to 32 teeth per inch. Use the former for heavy and the latter for thinner tubing. Then set the blade so that the teeth point forward.

To assure square-cut ends, make simple wood fixture to hold the tubing along with a slot to guide the saw blade. The cutting is done on the forward stroke only. Use light, easy strokes.

Sears, Roebuck

You can buy a tubing cutter that will handle up to 1½-inch stock for a little more than $3. Cutting blade is advanced by simply turning screw, as the tool is revolved around the tubing.

Chase Brass & Copper Co.

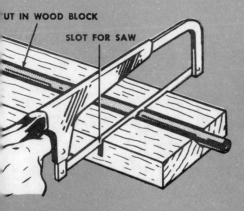

CUT IN WOOD BLOCK

SLOT FOR SAW

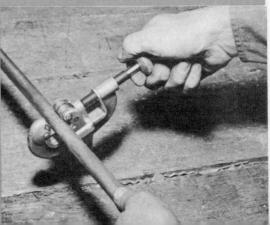

Cutting tube creates burr which must be removed, or the flow through pipe will be slowed and clogging will be encouraged. Almost all tubing cutters have built-in reamer for this purpose.

Chase Brass & Copper Co.

Tubing and fitting sockets must be cleaned before soldering. Clean them even if they appear to be bright and shiny. Use steel wool, fine emery or sand cloth, or special wire brush.

Some types of soldering flux must be stirred before using. Some contain a cleaner so that burnishing copper before soldering is unnecessary. Shown is a very popular soldering paste.

Apply the soldering flux to the cleaned tubing ends and then to the fittings. Put each piece of tubing into its fitting; then revolve the tubing so that flux is distributed evenly all over.

For average home plumbing use, solid wire 50/50 solder is the best. It is half tin, half lead. Approximate amount of solder needed for a joint is equal to the diameter of the tubing.

Apply heat to joint until the solder melts freely when touched to the metal. The solder will be drawn into the joint regardless of whether it is being fed down, up, or to the side.

Once you have the knack of working with copper, you can use your skill for such things as extending your heating system. The radiant baseboard heater is merely finned copper tubing.

Here finned copper tube used in baseboard heating is soldered to return line to boiler. Low-cost Type M copper tubing is especially designed for use in home radiant heating systems.

Flexible copper tubing has a special advantage in remodeling home plumbing because it can be snaked through walls. By use of bending spring, it's readily bent, eliminates fittings.

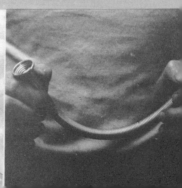

so you save on the cost of heating water

For drainage lines, type L, or lighter weight DWV tubing is used. The initials DWV stand for drainage, wastes, vents. Special drainage fittings are used for drainage and waste sections, but regular fittings may be used for the vent sections, which carry gases only. With the exception of shower and floor drains, which are usually 2 inches, and toilet drains which must be 3 to 4 inches, other drain and vent lines are usually 1½ inches. Main stacks are of 3-inch tubing, sometimes 4.

Measuring, Cutting, Bending. In measuring the length of pipe required in order to make a connection, measure the distance from the face of one fitting to the face of the other fitting. Then, add on the depth of the hub in each fitting.

Remember that if a piece of tubing is cut too long, you can always make another cut and shorten it to just the right length. If a piece is cut too short, however, and doesn't go all the way into the socket of the fitting, a perfect solder joint isn't possible. The moral: When in doubt, cut the tubing a little long, then refine your measure, perhaps by an actual test fitting.

Copper tubing may be cut either with a hack saw or with a tubing cutter. Since a cutter which will handle up to 1-inch tubing costs under $2, and one for up to 1½ inch costs only a little more than $3, it's a worthwhile tool to acquire if you have any considerable amount of plumbing to do. However, you can make good square cuts with a hack saw and a simple wood jig which you can knock together in just a few minutes. The slot in the jig will guide your saw blade, and the V-cut will steady the tubing. Some vises are equipped with guides for hack-saw blades and can be used for cutting tubing square.

Use a fine-toothed blade in the hack saw, one with 24 to 32 teeth per inch, the former for heavier tubing, the latter for thinner stuff. Set the blade so the teeth point forward. Cutting is done only on the forward stroke. Use light, easy strokes. After cutting tubing, remove burrs inside it with a file or with a reamer.

Rigid copper can be bent with a special tool. The tool is too expensive for the nonpro to buy, but you may find it useful if you can borrow one. Flexible tubing is easily bent by hand. Bend it slowly and in a wide radius to prevent kinking. To prevent kinking on sharp bends near the end of a section of tubing, you can insert a special spring steel bending tube to prevent wall collapse. A set of six bending tubes for bending tubing from ¼ to ⅝ inch diameter costs under $1.50 at Sears.

TYPICAL SOLDER-TYPE FITTINGS

TYPICAL RIGID-COPPER-PIPE FITTINGS

TYPICAL FLARE-TYPE FITTINGS

Soldering Joints. There are six simple steps in making a good solder joint.

1. Thoroughly clean and brighten the end of the tube and the socket of the fitting. Clean them even if they look clean and shiny. Use steel or fine emery or sand cloth or a special wire brush made for the purpose. Don't use a file. It's too coarse. The tube end must be round, in no way flattened or dented.

2. Apply a thin coat of flux or soldering paste to the cleaned end of the tube and to the fitting. Some flux must be stirred thoroughly before use. You can also get a preparation that combines flux and cleaner so that removal of oxidation from pipe and

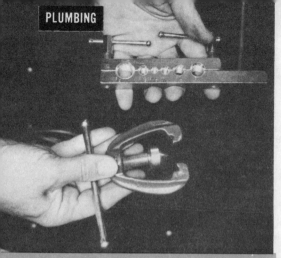

Flaring tool with screw yoke makes it possible to have perfect flared joints every time. The model shown here will handle six sizes of tubing, ranging from 3/16 to ⅝ inch, outside diameter.

General Hardware Mfg. Co.

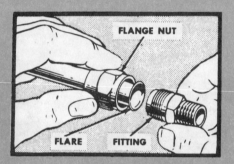

FLANGE NUT

FLARE   FITTING

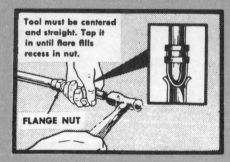

Tool must be centered and straight. Tap it in until flare fills recess in nut.

FLANGE NUT

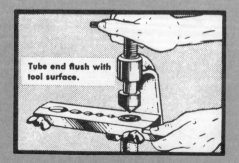

Tube end flush with tool surface.

fittings is unnecessary. Be sure the tubing fits all the way up against the stop in the socket.

3. Place the tube in the fitting. Revolve it once or twice to spread the flux. Several joints and fittings which all go together in one assembly can be prepared, then soldered in one operation. But never let fluxed joints stand more than 2 or 3 hours before soldering.

4. Apply heat to the fitting with torch, moving the flame so as to distribute the heat uniformly. On large fittings, such as on a soil stack, it is a good idea to apply two flames, one on each side to get uniform heating. Avoid overheating. It may burn the flux and destroy its effectiveness, making it necessary to reclean and reflux. Overheating cast fittings may cause them to crack.

5. When end of wire solder is touched to the joint, it should melt on contact, flow in and fill the fitting immediately, even if the solder has to travel sideways or straight up. Apply solder at one or two points only. Do not feed it around the full circumference of the tube.

When a line of solder shows completely around the joint, it's full up. Some plumbers like to add a fillet around the joint. Don't apply flame to the solder, and don't continue to heat the joint once you're applying solder. If you do, liquid solder is likely to keep running through the joint. With tubing longer than 1¼ inch, to assure equal distribution of solder, it is recommended that the fitting be moved, or the tube be tapped, while the solder is fed. While the joint is still hot, wipe away surplus solder with a rag or brush.

6. Allow joint to cool without disturbing it. Don't run water through the tubing until it has cooled. Cold water on a hot cast fitting may crack it. If, on testing, the joint leaks, the tube has to be completely drained before you can reheat the joint to solder-melting temperature. Any residual water will prevent it. When doing a solder joint near an already completed joint, it may be necessary to wrap the already finished joints with rags to keep their solder from melting.

Flare-Type Fittings. These are made with soft-temper tubing and are used where joints may occasionally have to be disconnected and remade, or where fire hazard makes soldering a joint impractical. Flare type fittings have threaded flange nuts which hold the fitting and pipe together.

Flaring can be done with either a flaring tool or a flanging tool. Before flaring the tubing remove the coupling nut from the

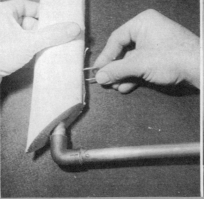

Insulation of hot water lines will reduce your fuel bills. Used on the cold water lines, insulation will prevent any sweating. Fiberglas type shown costs about 75c for 3 ft.

Insulation can help prevent frozen pipes. Popular felt type of insulation is attached with clips, can be mitered, as shown, for trim fit at elbows. Other joints are neatly wrapped.

"No Drip" insulation is brushed on cold water lines to prevent sweating. It can be especially useful on pipes which are concealed in walls. Is also available in tape form.

J. W. Mortell Co.

Variety of hangers are available for use with copper tubes. Hangers should be placed no more than 6 feet apart for rigid ½-inch tubing. Soft tubing requires closer support.

Pipe strap can be bought in rolls 10-feet long for about 50 cents. It can be used to secure any size tubing. It is readily bendable, and closely spaced holes make attaching easy.

Water supply lines must be securely supported, but not so tightly as to prevent expansion and contraction. Wire hangers are especially good in meeting these requirements.

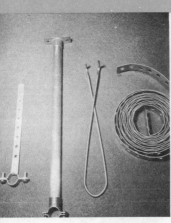

fitting and slide the nut onto the tubing. Drop some oil on the tube end, insert the flaring tool straight and centered, and tap tool with a hammer until the flare fills the recess in the nut. The nut can now be screwed onto the fitting threads.

Use a pair of adjustable or open-end wrenches to do the tightening, placing one on the body of the fitting to hold it, while the other tightens the nut. Tightening the nut forces the flared end of the tubing up against the rounded end of the fitting, making a tight seal.

In using a flanging tool, the tube should be inserted so its end is flush with the tool.

Hangers. On rigid copper tubing, hangers should be placed no more than six feet apart for ½ inch, eight for ¾ and 1 inch, and ten feet for 2 inch. Soft copper tubing requires somewhat closer spacing to prevent sagging.

Supply lines must be securely supported or they may vibrate and create noise, but hangers or clamps should not fit so tightly that they prevent expansion and contraction. Install water lines with a slight pitch, when necessary, to allow complete draining. •

WHAT YOU SHOULD KNOW ABOUT . .
galvanized steel and cast iron pipe

Oakum, hemp treated with pitch to make it moisture-proof, is yarned into cast-iron joints to within about 1 inch from the top. Joints are then filled with molten lead brim to the top.

YOU CAN USE threaded galvanized steel pipe for both water supply and drainage lines. Though the labor involved in installing it is more than required for copper, the initial cost of steel for water-line piping is lower than any other. For drainage, only service-weight cast iron costs less than steel. A package steel drainage system for a one-story house with a basement costs around $60. A copper system costs $80. A cast-iron system with service-weight pipe costs approximately $50.

Steel is somewhat lighter than cast iron, and is usually easier to install in remodeling jobs. Sold by mail order houses, pipes in packaged systems are cut and threaded to your exact specifications, so all you have to do is to assemble. Steel water pipe is usually no different from drainage pipes, but fittings are of special design.

Measuring and Cutting Steel Pipe. In measuring the length of pipe required for a connection, allowance must be made for the distance its threads go into fittings. To get the correct length, measure from the face of one fitting to the face of the next, then add the amount of thread length needed as indicated by the accompanying table. In working with ¾-inch pipe, for example, an extra half inch is needed for screwing into a fitting. This amounts to a full extra inch of length, above the face-to-face measure, when the pipe is screwed into a fitting at each end.

In screwing a pipe into a fitting, not all the threads are used. To try to use them all may result in splitting the fitting.

All threaded-pipe connections are made up quite tight. Large wrenches make the job easier. Note here how the pipe itself is used as a brace to steady connection while fitting is turned on.

Pipe vise is best tool for holding pipe while turning on a fitting. It is important to screw the fitting on as far and as tightly as possible, but not so tight as to (very possible!) split the fitting.

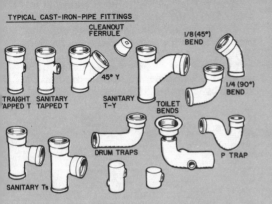

TYPICAL CAST-IRON-PIPE FITTINGS

CLEANOUT FERRULE

1/8 (45°) BEND

45° Y

STRAIGHT TAPPED T

SANITARY TAPPED T

SANITARY T-Y

TOILET BENDS

1/4 (90°) BEND

DRUM TRAPS

P TRAP

SANITARY Ts

For tightening most pipe and fittings, two pipe wrenches are needed. One holds the pipe in a fixed position while the other wrench turns the fitting on. Foot can be used to pin one wrench.

TYPICAL GALVANIZED MALLEABLE FITTINGS

T

90° L (REDUCING)

T (REDUCING)

90° L

REDUCER

PLUG

BUSHING

GROUND-JOINT UNION

45° L STREET

45° L

PIPE CAP

EXTENSION PIECE

90° L STREET

COUPLING

CROSS

FLOOR FLANGE

Pipe Size (inches)	Amount pipe is screwed into fitting (inches)	
	Standard fitting	Drainage fitting
½	½	—
¾	½	—
1	⅝	—
1¼	⅝	⅝
1½	⅝	⅝
2	¾	⅝
3	—	⅞
4	—	1

By careful planning, and making the most direct connections, you can reduce the number of fittings and the amount of pipe cutting and threading necessary. By use of nipples, short pieces of pipe already threaded and usually ranging in length from 1⅛ to 12 inches, you can further reduce the amount of cutting and threading.

If you are doubtful about pipe size, measure its circumference. If you don't have a tape measure, use a piece of string, then measure the string length with a ruler. The accompanying table gives pipe

Lighter than cast iron, steel is easier to use in remodeling jobs. If ordered from mail-order house, pipes can be cut and threaded to exact specifications. Note the variety of fittings shown above.

TYPICAL STEEL-PIPE FITTINGS

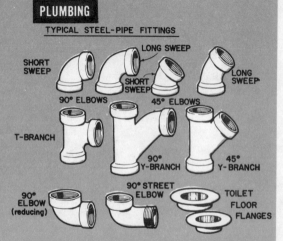

Steel water pipe is usually no different from drainage pipes, but the fittings are of a special design. Note better contours, smoother finish.

In calculating pipe length needed to complete a run, measure from the face of one fitting to the face of the next, then add or subtract thread needed for particular fitting.

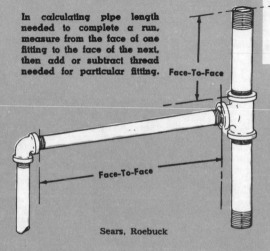

Face-To-Face

Face-To-Face

Sears, Roebuck

Steel pipe can also be cut with a hack saw, but a portable saber saw with a metal-cutting blade is a great time-and-muscle saver. Ordinary vise and one hand are used to keep the pipe steady.

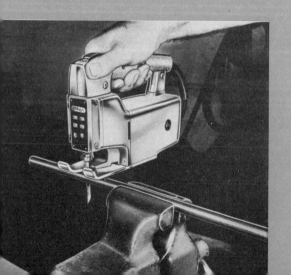

sizes based on string length. Use fittings the same size as the pipe.

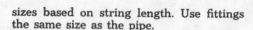

String length (inches)	2⅛	2⅝	3¼	4½	5¼	6
Pipe size (inches)	⅜	½	¾	1	1¼	1½

Steel pipe must be held rigidly for cutting and threading operations. A pipe vise is best for this purpose. Use a 24-teeth-to-the-inch blade in your hack saw for cutting, with its teeth directed foreward. Cut on the forward stroke only, and at a rate of about one stroke per second. Faster cutting may overheat the blade and it will break.

After cutting, remove burrs from the inside edge of the pipe end with a round file or a pipe reamer. Unreamed pipe ends increase resistance to water flow from 6 to 10 times.

In cutting with a pipe cutter, cut is made by gradually tightening up on the cutting wheel, by screwing in the handle, with each

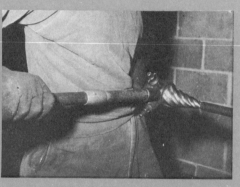

After cutting pipe, you'll find burrs along its inside edge. Get rid of them with a reamer. Burrs like these reduce the rate of flow through a pipe and make it very easy for clog-ups to develop.

Pipe vise on stand is convenient for working outdoors where length of piping poses no problems. The best way to cut steel pipe is with a wheeled cutter. The ends are then always exactly square.

revolution around the pipe. Apply cutting oil to the wheel as you work!

Threading and Joining. Full details on how to thread pipe are given in the chapter on "Plumbing Tools."

Never hold a threaded part with a wrench. It will damage the threads, and the resulting connection is likely to leak. If you must hold where the threads are, protect them by first putting two nuts on them, locked tight.

Always use pipe compound on threads in making connections. It helps insure against leak and will make the connection easier "to break" in the future if you want to take it apart. Cotton string is not usually used on threads, but if threads are imperfect, string may help make a tight connection. Put compound on male (external) threads only. If compound is put on the female (internal) threads, it is likely to get inside the pipe and start clogging. It may also work its way into valves and cause trouble.

Threads are tapered, so turning gets harder the farther you screw them in.

Larger wrenches make work easier. Note what large wrenches plumbers use.

A pipe vise can serve in place of a wrench for holding pipe firmly while a fitting is being turned on it. However, before making any assembly permanent, check to make sure you'll have necessary clearance for turning on other nearby fittings. You may have to revise the order in which you make connections.

Ordering Fittings. In asking for a fitting, always give the size first, then the name of the fitting. The size of a fitting and the size of the pipe used are always the same. Thus, a ¾-inch elbow is for ¾-inch pipe.

It is necessary to give the size of only one outlet on the fitting unless the outlets are of different sizes. In that case, give the larger first, the smaller second, and if there is an inlet or branch, name it third. If there are two branches, as in a cross fitting, the smaller of the two branches is named last.

Bushings are hexagonal fittings with both external and internal threads, and are used to connect a pipe or fitting of one size to a pipe or fitting of different size. In

You can have pipe threaded at a plumbing shop, but it's far more convenient to thread your own. You can do it with a tool borrowed from a mail-order house or rented from tool-rental agency.

Apply pipe joint compound to male (external) threads on pipe end, never to female (internal) threads. Compound helps make the joints tight against the leakage of either liquids or gases.

In ordering fittings, specify the same size as the pipe they are to fit. For reducing fittings, give larger or main outlet sizes first, then branch or smaller outlets—see sketch.

If pipe end isn't squarely cut, or if dies are worn or damaged, it may be difficult to cut good threads. Imperfect or damaged threads can often be salvaged with a little careful file work.

To assemble steel pipe over 2 inches in diameter use a chain wrench. Screw pipe as tightly as possible by hand. Place chain around pipe. Insert chain ends between tool prongs.

Sears, Roebuck

Nicholson Files

Sears, Roebuck

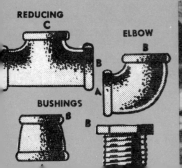

REDUCING
C

ELBOW

BUSHINGS

Pipe for holding

PIPE—FOR HOLDING

Tighten L and nipple together.

In making steel pipe assembly with chain wrench, make use of a pipe to hold your work against the thrust of the wrench. Here a toilet branch drain is being connected to a tee fitting in this fashion.

Sears, Roebuck

Even if you do use copper or steel pipe for your plumbing, you're almost certain to have to switch to cast iron where it goes underground. Look for C-I mark to be sure of industry's standard quality.

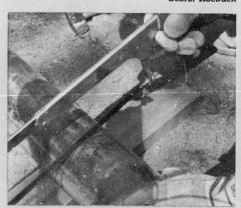

To cut service-weight cast-iron pipe, first mark line of cut all the way around pipe, using chalk or scratching pipe with a nail. With a hack saw, you can accurately score this line 1/16 inch deep.

To cut extra-heavy pipe, mark the line of cut by grooving with a triangular file. With pipe across a 2x4, use a hammer and chisel and continue cutting all around the pipe until it breaks evenly.

specifying a bushing, give its external size first, then the internal size.

External threads, as indicated previously, are known as male threads, internal as female. A street elbow is an elbow with male threads at one end, female at the other.

Unions are fittings designed so that a line can easily be disconnected. They are used near appliances, water heaters, water meters, and other equipment that may on occasion have to be pulled out. There are union tees and union elbows. Use these combination fittings and you can often save using two separate fittings.

A cap is used to close the end of a pipe. Plugs are used to close one end of a fitting.

Fittings used for drainage are different from those used for water pipes. They have no internal ledge or shoulder, and they have a pitch, corresponding to the pitch of the drainage or vent pipes with which they are used.

The name of a fitting sometimes changes. Fittings used on water pipes to change the direction of flow are called elbows. On drainage pipes they're called bends. A ¼ bend is the equivalent of a 90-degree elbow, a ⅙ bend is a 60-degree turn, and a ⅛ bend is a 45-degree turn. You can get bends with either short or long sweeps. The long sweep is a more gradual turn and reduces flow friction and resistance.

Cutting Cast-iron Pipe. Standard length is 5 feet. Use a double hub pipe when

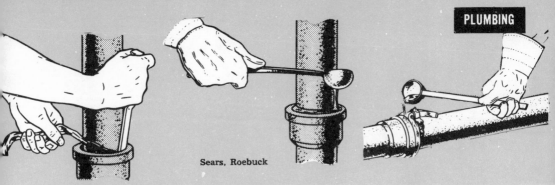

Sears, Roebuck

In joining cast iron, be sure both pipes are in perfect alignment and that joint is same size all around. With yarning tool, pack joint tightly with oakum to within 1 inch of the top. To avoid the danger of spattering lead, wear gloves, avert eyes and face, and extend ladle as far as possible from body. In one continuous pour, fill joint until the lead stands slightly above rim. See middle picture, above. Horizontal, even upside-down joints, can be poured by means of a joint runner (top right picture). Fit it tight against bell and, if necessary, use putty or clay around space to prevent leakage of lead from joint.

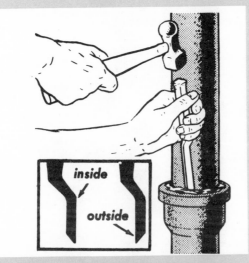

After the lead cools, inside and outside caulking irons pack it tightly back against the pipe and surrounding bell. Don't pound too hard or you may loosen the lead mass instead of tightening it.

Caulking Joints. Cast iron is connected by caulking. Place the spigot end of one pipe into the bell end of the following pipe, using a level to be sure it is straight and true. Some codes require 1 inch of lead in a joint, others permit ¾ inch. For an inch of lead, use one pound of lead for each inch of pipe diameter, per joint. For ¾ inch of lead, allow 1½ pounds of lead for a 2-inch pipe, 2¼ pounds for a 3-inch pipe, and 3 pounds for a 4-incher.

The best way of melting lead is with a plumber's furnace. Put the lead in the pot, small end down. It melts quicker that way. Be sure all equipment is dry. Moisture causes lead to sputter and splash out. You can also melt lead by merely playing an ordinary propane torch on a lead pot, or even a properly supported ladle.

While lead is melting, use a yarning iron to pack the rope-like oakum into the bottom of the hub, exercising care to see that the joint space is equal all the way around. Oakum swells when wet, and helps make a tight seal. It also prevents lead from running into the pipe. You can get oakum in 27-inch lengths. One length is needed for 2-inch pipe, two lengths for 3-inch. After oakum is packed to within an inch (or ¾ inch) of the top, pour the lead on.

First heat the ladle by holding it alongside the melting pot for 5 or 10 seconds. Use of a cold or wet ladle can result in an explosion. So can pouring lead into a joint that is wet. When the ladle is warm, push the dross floating on top of the lead to one side, and dip the bright metal. Pour it, in a single, continuous operation, to the top of the hub, or better yet, so it stands slightly above the top rim.

For horizontal joints, use an asbestos or rubber joint-runner. This device keeps the lead from running out of the joint as it is poured. •

pieces shorter than that are needed. When this pipe is cut, each piece will have a hub, and thus be usable. In measuring length of pipe needed, allow for pipe which goes into the hub of the pipe following it. This amounts to 2½ inches for 2-inch pipe, 2¾ inches for 3-inch pipe, 3 inches for 4-inch pipe.

To cut service-weight pipe, groove it $\frac{1}{16}$-inch deep with a hack saw, then tap with a heavy hammer on the part to be lopped off until the pipe breaks at the groove. The pipe should be supported on the side of the groove opposite to where you are doing the tapping. A 2x4, or a mound of dirt, does nicely. To cut extra-heavy pipe, keep tapping with hammer and chisel all around the pipe until it parts.

Before attaching pipe to a fitting, a stainless steel clamp is slipped over the pipe end. Clamp is tightened on the smooth shank of the fitting behind serrations. Large pipes take two clamps.

Flexible plastic pipe weighs only ⅛ as much as iron pipe, is far easier to join and use. For any cold-water purpose, it is unexcelled. Its cost is lower, too. It is cut with saw or knife.

Flexible plastic pipe is readily joined to any threaded fitting by means of an adapter. Joining compound is put on adapter threads and it is turned into fitting. Pipe then goes on adapter.

TIPS ON USING . . .

flexible plastic pipe

THE DAY when the entire house will have plastic plumbing is not far off. Plastic pipe has already proved itself superior in many ways for cold-water lines, and its use for drainage systems is at hand. Plastic pipe is gaining widespread use for sewer lines. What we shall probably see in the immediate future is use of plastic plumbing for everything except hot water lines.

Work is still being done on developing a plastic pipe which is suitable for hot water. The newest plastic being used for the purpose is polypropylene. It seems good, but whether it can withstand 180° temperatures and water pressure for years without breaking down is still to be proved.

But plastic has been perfected for many uses. Here's how you can use plastic, save work and money, and get better plumbing.

You can't beat plastic pipe for water service lines, swimming pool plumbing, lawn sprinkler systems, and jet well installations. Polyethylene plastic pipe weighs only ⅛ as much as steel pipe. One man can easily carry a 300-foot coil of the 1-inch size.

Plastic pipe requires fewer joints, is far easier to work. You don't need pipe cutters or threading tools. You can cut plastic with any saw, often with just a sharp knife. Flexible polyethylene plastic pipe, such as that made by Orangeburg and others, is one of the most popular varieties. It is assembled by means of hard plastic fittings, and you need only a screwdriver for the

Flexible polyethylene plastic pipe is ideally suited for swimming pool plumbing, jet well installations, and lawn sprinkler systems. Shown in photo is attachment to sprinkler head.

Plastic pipe will withstand severely corrosive soil chemicals, high pressure, and is resistant to freezing. When you use it for lawn sprinklers, you don't have to drain lines in winter.

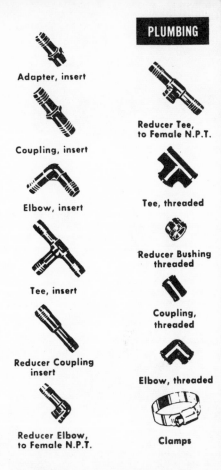

Adapter, insert

Coupling, insert

Elbow, insert

Tee, insert

Reducer Coupling insert

Reducer Elbow, to Female N.P.T.

Reducer Tee, to Female N.P.T.

Tee, threaded

Reducer Bushing threaded

Coupling, threaded

Elbow, threaded

Clamps

A variety of valves and fittings are available for use with plastic pipe. Shown are fittings for polyethylene pipe. All fittings are made of polystyrene plastic. Clamps are stainless steel.

Orangeburg Mfg. Co.

job. The pipe is made of high molecular weight polyethylene, the fittings of molded polystyrene.

How to Use Flexible Plastic Pipe. When flexible plastic pipe is used in a well installation, because of its very light weight, no special rig is needed for lowering the pipe down the casing, or for pulling it up again should repairs be necessary. Well casings themselves are being made of hard plastic. Because of the flexibility of the polyethylene pipe, no clearance is needed above a well for pulling up pipes. This makes it possible to put the well directly under the house.

Plastic pipe is not subject to rust, scale, or corrosion. It never has any "pipe taste." Its smooth interior surface means no turbulence and a minimum of resistance to water flow.

Polyethylene pipe is readily joined to threaded pipe or threaded fittings by means of adapters. When making a connection to a threaded fitting, the adapter is first screwed into the fitting. As a lubricant on the threaded end, Pipe-Tite Stik or Permatex No. 2 may be used. When the adapter has been turned in hand tight, it should be given one turn with an open-end wrench. Don't use a pipe wrench.

After putting a clamp loosely on the plastic pipe, push the fitting into the pipe up to its shoulder. Soaking the pipe-end in hot water for a minute will make it easier to insert the fitting. Screw the stainless steel clamp securely to the straight shank

Cutaway view of a cemented joint on PVC pipe. Cemented joints are by far the speediest kind to make, and are the preferred type. Such joints are stronger than the pipe itself without joints.

Sanding will eliminate burrs, assure tight fit. After sanding, clean pipe ends and fittings with rag dampened with a cleaner such as methyl ethyl ketone (MEK), acetone or similar ketone solvents.

To get a sound, leakproof joint, it is important to follow recommended procedures exactly. Use miter box to insure squarely-cut pipe ends. Ends must butt fully against fitting shoulder.

With a clean brush, apply special PVC solvent cement liberally to fitting, including shoulder of fitting, and butt end of the pipe. Small can of cement is good for countless number of joints.

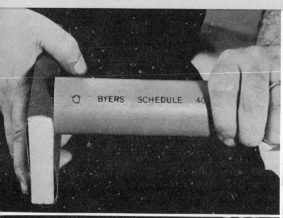

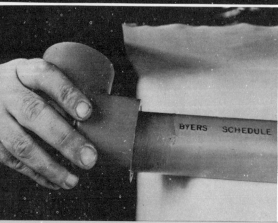

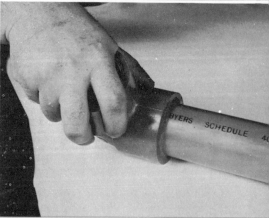

As soon as you finish applying cement, insert pipe into fitting and give it a ¼ (90°) turn. The time from start of cementing to completion of the ¼ turn must never exceed 1½ minutes.

Block the fitting tightly, or otherwise see that its position is held for several minutes, to insure a complete bond. Never disturb the bond by readjusting the pipe after the ¼ turn is made.

Though PVC pipe is rigid, it may readily be bent by application of heat. First pack the pipe with sand, or use a pipe-bending spring to support walls. Apply torch heat, but not right on pipe.

If pipe begins to scorch, you're holding it too close. Apply heat uniformly around pipe. When it begins to soften, bend it to desired angle, then hold it briefly while it cools and stiffens.

of the fitting *behind* the serrations. For pipe sizes over 1-inch, double clamping is recommended, with the second clamp placed *over* the serrations.

In placing flexible plastic pipe in a trench, be sure the trench bottom is free of sharp stones and other edged objects. Don't pull the pipe tight in the trench. Run it in a snake line, allowing at least one extra foot per 100 feet for thermal contraction. Don't make sharp bends with the pipe. If bends are necessary, use elbow fittings.

When the installation is complete, try it out under maximum pressure to see that all joints are secure and free of leaks, then backfill, using rock-free earth in the first six inches over the pipe. After that, backfilling can proceed as you please.

Installing PVC Pipe. For plumbing lines inside the house itself, one of the more popular varieties of plastic is PVC (polyvinyl chloride), such as that made by Byers, a company with a long-established reputation as a manufacturer of wrought-iron pipe. This rigid type of piping has been proven for cold-water systems, and is commercially available from coast to coast. PVC pipe was first developed in Germany in 1935, and has been widely used in Europe for more than twenty years.

PVC pipe can be joined by threading, or welding, but the simplest means of all is by cementing, sometimes called solvent welding. Solvent welding of PVC waste and vent lines takes only ¼ the time it takes to assemble bell-and-spigot pipe, and the pipe's weight is only ⅕ as much, making it far easier to handle and to support. Using this plastic pipe, a trained plumber can make every connection in a typical house in no more than ten minutes! Is it any wonder that the age of plastic plumbing is upon us?

In joining PVC pipe by cementing, be sure to cut pipe ends square, so they'll butt fully against the shoulder of the fitting. After cutting, sand the end of the pipe so it is smooth and will make full contact with the fitting shoulder.

Clean the pipe ends and fittings with a solvent, such as MEK (methyl ethyl ketone) or acetone. Using a clean brush, apply cement liberally to the fitting, its shoulder and to the butt end of the pipe. Insert the pipe into the fitting and give it a quarter turn. Important: No more than 1½ minutes must elapse from the time you start applying the cement until you complete the quarter turn. Don't disturb the pipe for several minutes after the quarter turn is made or you'll ruin the bond.

Drying of the cement is far enough advanced in from 16 to 24 hours to permit use of the line. The higher the air temperature, the quicker the drying time. Properly made, a cemented joint is stronger than the pipe itself.

PVC pipe may be readily bent. To do it, pack the pipe with sand, then heat it. You can use a torch for the purpose, but keep the pipe fairly far from the flame, so you don't overheat the material and scorch it. By exerting a little pressure, you can feel when the pipe has become soft enough for bending. Instead of sand, a metal spring, like that used in bending copper, may be used to support the pipe walls and prevent their flattening.

All plastic piping has a higher rate of thermal expansion than metal pipe, and the line must have enough freedom to move to accommodate changes in length. Expansion loops, or line offsets, can provide the necessary adaptability. Commercial expansion joints are also available for the purpose. ●

HOW TO PUT IN . . . drainage lines

Chase Brass & Copper Co.

The house drain is the large horizontal pipe that carries all plumbing wastes out beyond the house wall. Copper is the easiest kind of piping to use in making any good drainage connection.

IN NUMBER and size of pipes, the drainage system is by far the most important part of home plumbing, but the technique of installing, adding to, or remodeling it is not difficult.

In water pipes, the flow is under pressure. Drainage flows by gravity, and without pressure, so pipes must be large and have a steady downward slope toward point of disposal. Drainage lines must also be vented to the open air, for otherwise any movement of wastes through them would tend to create a vacuum which would slow down or stop the flow.

The large vertical drain lines which continue up through the roof as vents are called stacks, soil stacks if they receive any discharge from toilets, waste stacks if they do not. Similarly, horizontal drainage pipes are called soil lines or waste lines, depending on the source of the drainage they carry.

A Stack Is Needed. If you are adding a bathroom or a half bath, you will require a soil stack close at hand. In remodeling, it is to your advantage to connect up to an existing soil stack, if that is possible. If branch drain and vent lines are obsolete, or must be replaced, you can use DWV copper tubing for the purpose, and connect on to the existing cast iron stack by means of adapters. If you are adding only a sink or lavatory, you will need a waste stack for it. Since this is likely to be only 1½-inch pipe, it isn't a serious expense if you have to add a new one.

If you are installing a new soil stack, you can put it in a standard 2x4 partition, if you use copper. But if you are remodeling, it will probably be better to run your stack up outside a wall, instead of opening up a wall to do it, so the bulk of the piping material won't be so important. When you put a stack outside a wall, you can box it in. Covered with plasterboard and decorated like the rest of the room, the alteration will be scarcely noticeable, especially if it's in a corner. Stacks can also be run up through closets. In other cases, wall sections can be thickened inconspicuously, by setting new studs against existing wall studs.

In a new house, or new addition, of course, there is no problem of where to put a stack, or how to open up walls and floors so drainage lines can be run, but planning in any case can reduce the cutting of the

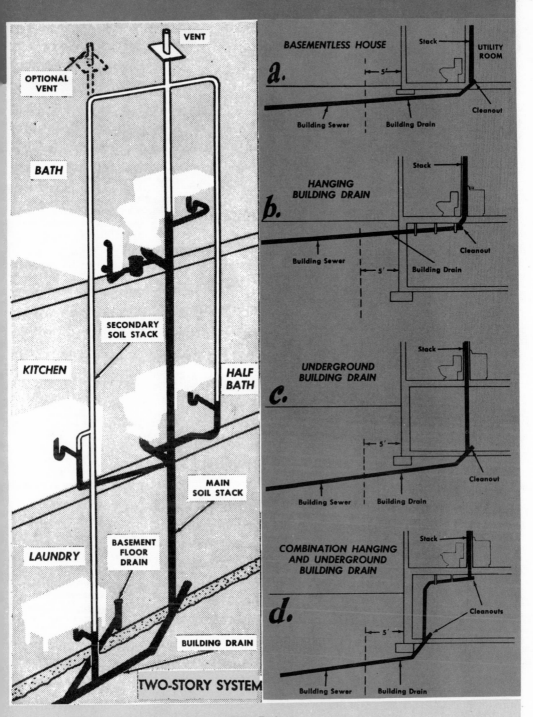

VENT

OPTIONAL VENT

BATH

SECONDARY SOIL STACK

KITCHEN

HALF BATH

MAIN SOIL STACK

LAUNDRY

BASEMENT FLOOR DRAIN

BUILDING DRAIN

TWO-STORY SYSTEM

a. BASEMENTLESS HOUSE

Stack

UTILITY ROOM

5'

Cleanout

Building Sewer

Building Drain

b. HANGING BUILDING DRAIN

Stack

Cleanout

Building Sewer

5'

Building Drain

c. UNDERGROUND BUILDING DRAIN

Stack

5'

Cleanout

Building Sewer

Building Drain

d. COMBINATION HANGING AND UNDERGROUND BUILDING DRAIN

Stack

Cleanouts

5'

Building Sewer

Building Drain

Sears, Roebuck

Study this layout and you will see how simple the drain-and-vent system for a two-story house can be, and the ease with which a first-floor half bath may be added to existing plumbing.

Here are four ways in which a drain and sewer line may be installed. And if you are adding a bathroom, you may find it simpler and better to add a second septic tank to handle its waste.

First step, left, when you install stack: Position closet bend attached to T plumb line. Then drop it through T and Y or a T-Y connected to house drain and center underneath it. Center photo, T-Y fitting includes cleanout ferrule. Top of T-Y fitting must be centered exactly under stack. Also align so it is exactly level. Right, T fitting, to which closet bend is attached, is caulked into T-Y of house drain. If there is a gap, insert pipe to bridge gap between the T-Y and the T. Study photos for installation details.

house structure to a minimum. Though cast-iron pipe diameter may be only 2, 3, or 4 inches, you have to consider that the bell end of each pipe section or fitting will be 4, 5¼ and 6¼ inches, respectively.

Steel pipe comes in long lengths, so it is sometimes possible to avoid fittings in the wall, and the pipe will then go into a minimum space. When planning fittings to go into a wall, don't overlook the clearance needed for turning the fitting within the space. Twice as much space is needed for turning a fitting as is required for the fitting alone. See the accompanying table for clearances required.

CLEARANCES NEEDED FOR STEEL PIPE
(inches)

Pipe Size	Pipe Alone	Pipe and Fittings	For Turning Fitting
1½	2	3	6
2	2½	3½	7
3	3½	5	10
4	4½	6	12

Toilet Drainage. Roughing-in dimensions for each fixture are supplied by the manufacturer. In the case of a toilet, these dimensions will tell you where the closet bend (the toilet drain) must go, and how far the center of its opening must be out from the wall.

On the first floor, if there is no ceiling below, a closet bend can be installed from underneath and there is need to cut only a hole where the branch drain connects to the toilet itself. If a new soil stack is being installed, a second hole will have to be cut for it.

If there is a ceiling on the room below, it is usually preferable to install the closet bend from above. Remove enough of the

flooring so that the drain, and the T of the stack to which it connects, can be set in place.

If installed from above, in this manner, don't permit the drain to rest on the ceiling. Rest the pipe on a cross brace, made either of a 2x4 or a metal strap. If installed from below, this drain also requires support. It can be a 1x4 or 2x4 nailed across the joints, or if the closet bend runs across the joists, a trapeze to support it can be made of 1x4's. In the latter case, an extension of the bend will also be needed to reach the floor above. The toilet floor flange, which is attached at the top of the bend, should rest on the finished floor.

If the bend is of cast iron, or is designed for fitting to cast iron, caulk it to the T before it is installed. In this way, the necessity for pouring a vertical lead joint is avoided.

The House Drain. If the stack is to connect to a new underground drain leading outside, drop a plumb bob through the center of the T, which has just been fixed in position, and locate the spot exactly under it. From this point a trench must be dug to the foundation wall where the drain will leave the house. You will probably have to break up a strip of the basement's concrete floor to do it. It can be patched up afterward.

The top of the drain pipe, when installed, should be approximately 1 foot below floor level at the stack, and slope 1 inch in each 5 feet to the basement wall. The house drain continues for 5 feet beyond the outside of the wall where it becomes the house sewer. To get through the wall, you'll have to break through it, or tunnel under it.

If there is to be a basement floor drain, it can connect to the house drain by means of a Y-fitting. If you have a septic tank, however, it is recommended than any base-

Ingersoll-Humphreys

Lead closet bends are better for they have certain amount of give. When testing completed drainage system for leaks, end of a lead bend is easily pinched together and sealed. Wall-hung toilets are popular and occupy no floor space. Center photo, hanger fitting of wall toilet is caulked into soil pipe fitting. Every part of house drain and sewer must be accessible to cleanout. Clean-out plug is needed at every change in direction. Cleanout here is in T-Y fitting. Note how Y fits closely, then into the wall.

When a house is built on a slab, all the major drain lines must be in place before concrete is poured. However, specially fitted toilets and baths can be installed with above-slab piping.

In remodeling, it's frequently best to make use of an existing soil stack, and attach new drain and vent lines to it. Shown are possible arrangements for one and 1½ bathroom installations.

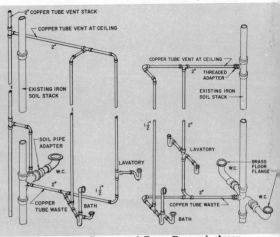

Copper and Brass Research Assoc.

ment floor drain empty into a separate dry well, or connect to the disposal field after the septic tank. It is inadvisable to flood a septic tank with too much waste water.

The base of the soil stack connects to the drain by means of a Y and a ⅛ bend. First, caulk the ⅛ bend to one section of cast iron pipe, then caulk the Y to it. Place this assembly so that the plumb bob from the T fitting above is centered directly over the middle of the Y opening. Check the top of the Y to see that it is exactly level. Concrete is now poured around the assembly to fix it in place.

After the concrete has set, the stack can be installed from the Y up to the T. Cut the last section of stack pipe, as required, so that the spigot end of the T will fit ex-

actly into the last section's hub. Raise the T just enough so that the fit can be made. A cleanout plug is caulked into the other branch of the Y.

If the house drain is suspended from the floor joists, the connection between the T at the closet bend and the drain can often be made with only a T-Y fitting. In other cases, you may have to insert a section of pipe between the T-Y and the T. In assembling the house drain, caulk two or three lengths of pipe together before hanging it and the job will be easier.

Completing the Stack. In completing the rest of the stack, insert sanitary T's at the proper height for branch drains to sink, lavatory, or tub, remembering that branch drains slope 1 inch in every 4 feet. Branch drains, using threaded steel pipe, are installed outward from the stack. A closet-bend-T assembly can be installed at the second floor for a toilet there.

Install standard T's for branch vent connections to suit your convenience. These don't require accurate positioning. Vent lines, using steel pipe, are assembled by starting one pipe upward from the branch drain being vented, and another pipe at the T in the stack. The two sections are joined by means of a long screw, or split coupling. One pipe end is threaded more than standard so that both parts of the split coupling can be turned onto it. The larger part of the split coupling is then turned back to join both pipes and wicking is used to seal between the two sections of the coupling.

If it is necessary to offset the stack in the drainage section, use ⅛ bends. Offsets in the vent section, perhaps needed to miss a roof rafter, can be made either with ⅛ or ¼ bends.

The stack should extend at least 6 inches above the roof, and the roof-pipe joint sealed with flashing. If the flashing is a prefab metal one, get one designed for the size pipe you are using and the pitch of your roof. New plastic flashing has many advantages. It is easier to use, and is likely to be longer lasting and less subject to leaking. Saraloy 400, a new plastic flashing material by Dow, is admirably suited for use on vents. Cut a hole ⅓ the size of the vent in a piece of the flashing. Coat the underside of the flashing and the roof surface with the special adhesive pro-

There is no limit to the ways in which drainage pipes can be arranged, provided pitch is maintained and sharp turns avoided. Left, a toilet is connected to a soil stack beyond stack base. In center photo, two toilets (left and right of pipe) are connected to one center stack by a 45° Double Y arrangement. A Long Turn 90° Double T-Y is frequently used in similar situations. Right, the 90° Double T-Y is used for joining two toilets to a single stack. Note how connections have been made below ceiling level, and how framing has been arranged to box all pipes in. Plan layouts carefully.

Because of copper's light weight, long sections of it can be assembled where it is convenient, then lifted into place. Below, fitting is a 3x3x1½-inch copper to copper to copper 90° T-Y. Perforated copper strap, ¾ inch wide, hangs this house drain to floor joists. Waste line, center photo, goes to kitchen sink. Note continuous pitch of the line, and how it is kept out of the way. By hanging house drain near ceiling and bringing it down only when it has to pass through house wall, maximum headroom is gained. At the wall, copper T-Y fitting is joined to cast iron, as shown in photo at far right, below.

Chase Brass & Copper Co. photos

vided, then stretch the flashing over the pipe and pull it down to make a bond with the roof. The bonded area should extend 6 inches out from the base of the vent stack. The flashing will fit the pipe very snugly and be absolutely weathertight.

Roofing should overlap vent flashing at the top and each side only. The lower side of the flashing overlaps the roofing. Where there is danger that frost might plug up a vent terminal, it must be not less than 3 inches in diameter. If you are using a secondary stack that is smaller than this size, use an increaser just below roof level so that it is at least 3 inches in diameter above the roof.

Drainage using copper tubing is simpler by far than that employing cast-iron pipe. Connections and fittings are essentially the same, but assembly is much easier. Joints are made by sweating, as described in the chapter on copper tubing, and take only a fraction of the time that is required for caulking cast iron joints. Weight of copper, too, is much less, so that bracing is less of a problem, and one man can handle long lengths or entire assemblies without difficulty.

Testing the Drainage System. When drainage lines are complete, they must be carefully tested to be sure all joints, both in the drain and vent sections, are absolutely tight. This must be done before walls or floors are enclosed. All pipe openings must be capped or plugged for the test.

Caps are used at the ends of most fixture drain lines. The toilet bend, if it is lead, can be sealed by pinching its top

Below left, 3-inch copper main vent stack fits in a standard 2x4 partition. Closet flange in foreground is soldered to a closet bend which in turn is joined by a T fitting to the stack. Sanitary tee fitting connects to kitchen sink trap, center. Fitting below is a cleanout. Vent line extends upward, connects to main stack. Branch vents often connect to inlet in stack increaser. New plastic flashing makes installation of shower pans easy for the nonprofessional plumber. Pans are quickly joined with a special solvent. Clamping ring connects it to shower drain.

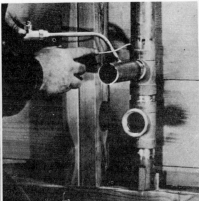

Dow Chemical Co.

When all drainage and vent lines have been completed, they are filled with water brim to the top of roof vents. Then all joints are carefully checked, photo below, to see if there are any leaks. Twin lavatories are gaining favor because they greatly increase usefulness of a bathroom. Center, drain connections for the two basins are easily joined to single pipe with a Double T-Y fitting. Branch vent lines may be joined to main vent stack at almost any convenient height. To save on number of fittings needed, join two branch vent lines to stack with 3x3x1½x1½-inch 90° Double T-Y (center photo, below).

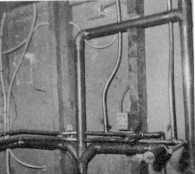

Possible basement plumbing installation for an automatic washing machine, above left. A trap is attached to a branch waste line with a 90° T-Y copper to compression joint with a metal ring. Toilet is attached to closet bend by means of a closet flange. Flange may be soldered to copper tube or to a 90° street elbow. Flange may be protected during construction by a wooden cover. In freezing weather, a vent terminal less than 3 inches in diameter is likely to be clogged by frost. To avoid that, use increaser fitting to enlarge small vent stacks to at least 3 inches, as shown at top right.

Where the house drain is below basement floor level, a floor drain may be connected to it. Where house drain is hanging one, best solution is to install a sump for basement drainage. Sump pit is a tile pipe sunk in floor. Float starts pump running whenever water level rises beyond certain point. Arrangement like this is first-rate insurance against flooded basement. In testing completed drainage system for leaks, house drain is usually sealed by means of a test plug. Rubber stopper on device is spread when it is compressed, fills end of pipe watertight, shown in photo at right, directly above.

House sewer line should connect to city sewer in street as directly as possible, and should preferably have pitch of two per cent, or about ¼ inch per foot, but ⅛-inch pitch is acceptable.

House sewer line can be made of cast iron, clay, cement, cement-asbestos, plastic, or bituminous fiber pipe. Below, a new cement-asbestos pipe is assembled by means of a special adhesive.

Johns-Manville

together and soldering it. Otherwise, a test plug can be borrowed from a plumbing shop for the purpose. The house drain, too, is similarly plugged. Plugs have a rubber spreader placed between two flanges. By turning a wing nut, the rubber is expanded to greater diameter, sealing the pipe.

The entire drainage and venting system is filled with water through the stacks on the roof. Water should be allowed to remain in the pipes at least 12 hours and all joints carefully inspected for leaks. The plumbing inspector will make his investigation while the system is filled, so call him when you are ready.

If any joints need remaking, the water first has to be drained out to below the level of the joint, for it is impossible to solder any pipe or remake any joint containing water. If you fill stacks brimful, leaks will quickly make themselves known by a sharp lowering of the water level.

The House Sewer. This is a continuation of the house drain from a point 5 feet outside the foundation wall. The house sewer continues either to the city sewer or past the septic tank to the beginning of the disposal field or leaching wells.

The house sewer line may be cast iron, clay, concrete, cement-asbestos, plastic, or bituminous fiber pipe, depending on local code requirements and your own preference. It is usually 4 inches in diameter, and never smaller than the house drain.

The trench in which it is laid is usually from 5 to 6 feet deep and 2 feet wide. It should be as straight as you can make it. If a bend is required, it should be a grad-

ual one. For making a right-angle turn, use either a long-sweep ¼ bend, or two 45-degree L's, with a cleanout.

A cleanout is required for every 50 feet of sewer line, and for any change in pitch greater than 22½ degrees. Cleanouts are installed in T fittings inserted in the sewer line. A cleanout ferrule or plug is installed at ground level.

The sewer preferably should have a pitch of 2 per cent, approximately ¼ inch per foot, but a pitch of only 1 per cent, approximately ⅛ inch, is sometimes permissible. To get the correct pitch, stretch a line and level it, using a line level. Every ten feet, the ditch will be about 2½ inches deeper if the pitch is 2 per cent. Use a marked pole for ease in measuring the depth.

The depth of the connection to be made at the city sewer must, of course, be determined before you can decide on the grade required for the house sewer. Depth of the city sewer may be determined by removal of manhole covers on both sides of the proposed connection, and lowering a long stick. The depth of the sewer at your lot front can then be calculated.

If it is necessary to pitch a house sewer more than ¼ inch per foot, restrict the steeper part of the grade to the section between the house and the curb line, then reduce the grade to a ¼ inch between the curb and the city sewer.

Connection of the house sewer to the city sewer is usually made by a representative of the appropriate city department, or by a contractor under bond.

New plastic flashing is effective means of sealing stack-roof joint. Neoprene type is shown in left and center photos. At the right. completed installation is made with Saraloy 400, another plastic.

DuPont photos   Dow

water pipes

. . . AND HOW TO INSTALL THEM

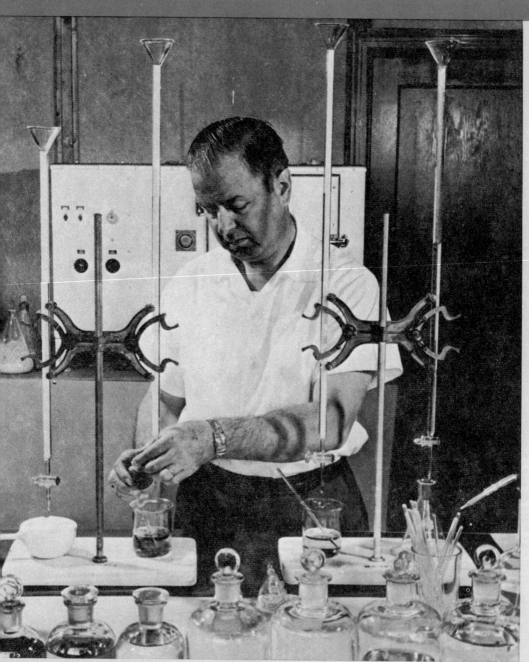

Chase Brass & Copper Co.

Consider the type of water in your area when deciding which kind of piping to use. Copper is best in most sections. Here a metallurgist studies effects of various waters on copper.

2288

THE PIPE which brings water into the house, either from a private well or from city mains, is known as the water service line. The minimum size of this line is ¾ inch. It will deliver up to 10 gallons per minute, which is usually considered sufficient for from 1 to 10 fixtures. A 1-inch pipe will deliver up to 18 gallons per minute and is considered adequate for up to 20 fixtures.

A ¾-inch main will supply two ½-inch branches. A 1-inch main will supply two ¾-inch branches.

Running the Service Line. Tapping the city water main is usually done by the water company, and requires a special tool which plumbers do not have. The water service line to the house must be laid on undisturbed earth below the frost line. If it is laid on backfill, settlement can cause rupturing of the pipe.

If the pipe cannot be laid below the frost line, it sometimes can be adequately protected by insulation. Aside from safeguarding the pipe from freezing, having it 3 to 4 feet deep will protect it from damage should trucks or other heavy vehicles cross the area. It is best never to run a house service line under a driveway.

Type K flexible copper tubing is a good

Important things to watch in water-pipe installation: run pipe as directly as possible, use adequate size pipe, use minimum number of fittings.

By using flexible Type K copper tubing for house water-service line, excavation to avoid boulders, tree roots and other obstructions can be avoided.

Water meter, if required, may be placed in water-service line near curb, or right inside house. Curb stop (shut-off) is on street side of the meter.

Mueller Brass Co.

Outdoor water meter is often installed in a protective box. In some cases, the curb stop may be reached by removing the cover, as shown here. It can then be turned on or off by special key.

Pressure reducing valve is important where water pressure is in excess of 80 pounds per square inch, or where it fluctuates widely. By adjustment, you can set this valve at any pressure.

Where water pressure is low, use pump and tank like those used in pumping well water. Usual range of pressure is from 20 to 40 pounds p.s.i.

One-inch main supplies hot and cold-water needs. Individual hot and cold line are ¾ inch, reduced to ½ inch for branch lines supplying fixture groups.

Plan water and drainage lines together. Risers carry water from floor to floor. They can be placed in same stud space used for drainage, stack lines.

choice for the water service line, for it comes in long lengths and usually can be laid without joints from city main to the house. Though it is advisable to run the line as straight and direct as possible, when necessary the flexible tubing can be readily curved around boulders or other obstructions. Galvanized wrought iron is also widely used in many areas for water service.

Where codes permit, plastic pipe performs excellently as a water service line. Cost of ¾-inch Type K copper is about 60 cents per foot. The same size in plastic pipe costs little more than 10 cents per foot, is available in rolls up to 2000 feet long.

The water service pipe may be placed in the same trench as the house sewer pipe if it's kept at least 12 inches above the sewer line. This is best done by placing the water pipe on a solid shelf at one side of the trench. It is important to keep joints in the water pipe to a minimum.

A corporation stop, for turning off the water, is screwed into the hole made in the water main by the tapping machine. A section of flexible pipe, commonly known as a gooseneck, connects it to a curb stop, another shutoff, which is placed between the street curb and the property line. This stop can be reached with a long key after removing the cover of the gate box placed above it. From here to the house, the water service pipe slopes upward. This permits draining it, when necessary.

The service line comes up through the basement floor or passes through the foundation wall. Use a masonry drill, or a star drill and hammer, for cutting a foundation opening. After the pipe has been passed

through, caulk around it with a bituminous caulking compound. Don't use mortar. Flexibility is important. In a basementless house, entry is commonly made into a utility room.

Inside the House. It is common practice to install a ground key valve, with a drain, on the service just inside the house. It functions as a handy shutoff when repairs are being made to the house plumbing.

If water pressure is over 80 lbs. psi (per square inch), installation of a pressure-reducing valve is recommended. Its cost: about $15. It will prevent pipe noises, water hammer, and save wear-and-tear on pipes and fittings. With the pressure-reducing valve, the water can be kept at a uniform 40 lbs. psi around the clock, or set at any other pressure desired.

Next in the line comes the meter, if one is required. It will be installed by a representative of the water company. Alternately, a meter may be installed at the corporation stop in the street.

Where water pressure is below requirements, a pump and pressure tank can be installed to bring the pressure up to the desired level. It is similar to equipment used in pumping water from a well.

On the house side of the water meter, a gate or ground-key valve is installed, followed by a globe valve which can be used for draining water from all pipes in the house if the house should ever be unheated during freezing weather. The valve is often installed on a short spur line so it in no way interferes with the flow of water through the main. All horizontal lines in the house system have a slight slope back to this point.

Split shingles are useful in aligning pipes in holes. Pipes should have room for expansion movement, but not enough leeway to rattle or vibrate.

Standard rough-in height for shower is 76 inches, with shower head at about 66 inches. Most women prefer shower head at about 60 inches. Suit yourself.

Shown: typical water pipe connections to bathtub are: hot water left, cold right, tub spout between. Plug at top is for shower, if one is used.

Planning Water Distribution. Plan your water lines in the house so that they travel the most direct route to fixtures. Directness is important, for each turn adds friction and loss of water pressure. Be sure the pipe is of adequate size. Adequate pipe size is important not only for a full flow at fixtures, but for proper operation of washing machines and dishwashers.

Piping that is too small is subject to water noises, vibration, and water hammer. If there isn't enough flow, water demand in one part of the house may cause an abrupt slackening of flow elsewhere. If anyone is in a shower when this happens, the results can be serious scalding. If you are using copper, in average circumstances plan on ¾-inch tubing for main hot and cold water lines, ½-inch for branch lines to all fixtures, with the exception of lavatories and toilets which are adequately served by ⅜-inch tubing.

Supply lines can be run across the bottom of floor joists, or parallel to joists and between them. Where lines run across joists, furring strips can be used to bring the ceiling level below the pipes. Lines can also be run across the top of joists by notching the joists.

Use a minimum number of joints and fittings. It will mean less work, less cost, less possibility of leakage, and reduction in resistance to water flow. You can eliminate some joints by use of flexible tubing for risers. Risers are vertical pipes which extend from one floor to the next. Use rigid tubing for horizontal lines. It's neater, and there's no danger of sags, which might trap water and prevent draining of the line, should that ever be necessary.

Where these water pipes cross drain lines they have been soldered together. This is to prevent pipe movement, which might be noisy, and which could eventually wear a hole and cause a leak.

A good antihammer air chamber is made of tubing one size larger than the line it serves. In this case, 1-inch tubing is used for the chamber on a ¾-inch line. Chamber is about 12 inches high.

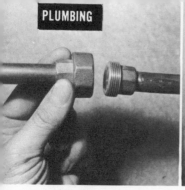

At water heaters, water softeners, dishwashers, filters, it is advisable to insert union in lines so pipes can be easily disconnected for any servicing. This will save headaches later.

On body of a stop-and-waste valve, arrow points in the direction water should flow through valve for correct installation. By opening knurled cap, water can then be drained.

Mansfield Sanitary, Inc.

Outside hose cocks subject to freezing require a shut-off valve inside the house. Frost-proof wall hydrants, however, like the one shown, can be safely left on in any season.

Latest push-button faucet control simplifies supply lines, as mixing of the hot and cold water is done at the heater and only one line need be run to each faucet. Flow is controlled.

In typical basement or crawl-space installation water lines are run across or between joists. Where to locate the hot water tank is an important part of your planning. It usually goes near kitchen.

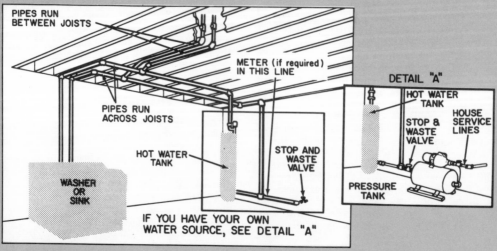

PIPES RUN BETWEEN JOISTS

METER (if required) IN THIS LINE

DETAIL "A"

PIPES RUN ACROSS JOISTS

HOT WATER TANK

HOUSE SERVICE LINES

STOP & WASTE VALVE

HOT WATER TANK

STOP AND WASTE VALVE

WASHER OR SINK

PRESSURE TANK

IF YOU HAVE YOUR OWN WATER SOURCE, SEE DETAIL "A"

2292

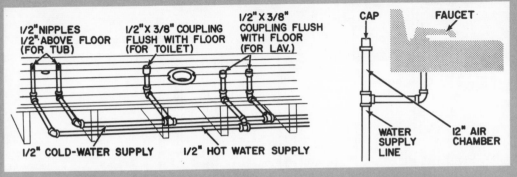

Water lines need not be run up through walls to serve first-floor fixtures. They can be brought up through floor, as shown. By use of a cabinet lavatory, the piping to it is easily concealed.

An air chamber is a dead-end section of pipe in which air is trapped. It absorbs the shock of water flow suddenly being stopped. A separate chamber is usually provided for every faucet.

You can also save on the number of fittings by using combination types. For example, you can use a union-tee or a union-ell instead of separate union and tee or ell fittings.

When installing both water pipes and drainage pipes, plan them together. Frequently water pipes can pass through the same openings provided for the larger drainage lines. Supply lines to a second-floor bathroom usually are run up next to the stack, the large vertical drain and vent pipe that extends up through the roof. Avoid contact between pipes and electrical cables. Such grounding may cause interference on radio and TV. When touching is unavoidable, wrap the point of contact with insulating tape. In walls, run branch lines through notches cut in partition studs.

Keep hot and cold water lines a minimum of 6 inches apart. If they are closer, the hot water line will lose heat to the cold one, and the cold one will sweat. If the pipes can't be separated, insulate them. Avoid running water pipes in exterior walls if there is any danger of their freezing there. If they are run there, always place wall insulation between the pipes and the exterior sheathing.

In areas where the summer climate is humid, always insulate cold water lines which run through walls or floors. It will prevent their sweating and discoloring paint or wallpaper on walls or ceiling, may even be necessary to safeguard the wall or ceiling structure itself. One of the easiest types of insulation to apply for this purpose is NoDrip Plastic Coating. It is brushed on. Further details on pipe insulation may be found in the chapter on plumbing noise.

Plan water lines with the location of your water heater in mind. If the heater is oil- or gas-fired it will have to be placed near a chimney or vent. Electric heaters, of course, do not need this provision. The heater, in any case, should be as close as possible to kitchen and bathrooms to minimize long runs of hot water pipes and attendant losses in heat. Where bathrooms are widely separated, two heaters may be both a convenience and an economy.

Hot water pipes are always connected to the left-hand faucet on sinks, lavatories, and other fixtures. Keep this in mind when bringing pipes up to the fixture. Where bathrooms are back-to-back, or where there are basins on two sides of a partition, pipes have to be crossed over if conventional, old-style faucets are used. However, with a Moen-style single-control faucet, no crossing is necessary. The faucet handle is merely taken off and reinstalled 180 degrees from its original position. That reverses its hot and cold inlets, but doesn't affect its operation otherwise.

Where water pipes attach to a hot water heater, pool filter, dishwasher, water softener, or other device that may on occasion have to be disconnected for servicing, put a union in each line. The connection can then easily be taken apart or made, whenever or as often as necessary, by merely turning the hex nut.

Adding New Branches. Do you want to install a basement shower, an automatic clothes washer or dishwasher, add an extra sprinkling outlet, a drinking fountain? The easy way to do it is with "Quick-Tee" connectors. The same connectors can also be used for making air, vacuum and gas connections. A neoprene gasket between the connector and the pipe makes the joint leakproof. Connectors are available for ½- and ¾-inch iron pipe and ⅝-inch OD

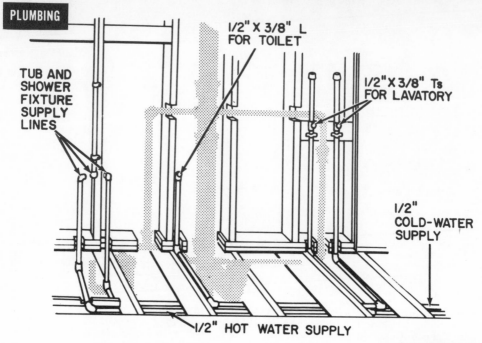

1/2" X 3/8" L
FOR TOILET

TUB AND
SHOWER
FIXTURE
SUPPLY
LINES

1/2" X 3/8" Ts
FOR LAVATORY

1/2"
COLD-WATER
SUPPLY

1/2" HOT WATER SUPPLY

Sears, Roebuck & Co.

A typical installation, where the supply pipes are brought up through the wall to the fixtures, looks like this. Note how the plate (the doubled member under the studs) is notched to accommodate pipes.

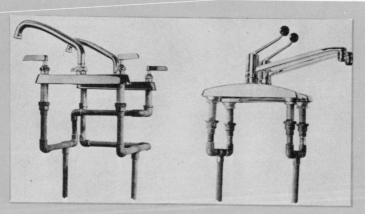

When two sinks are installed on opposite sides of a partition, piping has to be crossed over, as on left, if ordinary faucets are used. By use of Moen-style faucets, right, piping is simpler.

Adding a basement shower, a hose cock, or installing a clothes washer or a dishwasher is greatly simplified by the use of the new saddle-type tees. They may be used on either copper or iron pipe.

BASEMENT SHOWER | EXTRA SPRINKLING OUTLET | AUTOMATIC WASHER | AUTOMATIC DISHWASHER

In six easy steps, as shown in photos, the water is shut off, the tee is attached to the pipe, and a ¼- or ⅜-inch hole drilled. A threaded hosecock, or any other threaded connection may then be made.

(outside diameter) copper tubing (shown).

In industry these tee fittings are used for making quick connections for air-operated power tools; on the farm, for installation of milking machine stations. They have many non-plumbing applications, as well, such as use as brackets for iron pipe handrails, and hanging signs from pipe.

In making a water pipe connection with one of these tees, first turn off the water in the pipe. Sand or steel-wool the pipe to remove scale or dirt. Clamp the connector to the pipe and tighten its hex nuts. The connector used on copper tubing has screws.

Drill a ¼- or ⅜-inch hole in the pipe in the fitting's threaded opening. Blow out any metal chips. Now add a faucet, branch pipe, or any other threaded pipe fitting. Turn on the water, open the faucet to flush it out. That's all there is to it. •

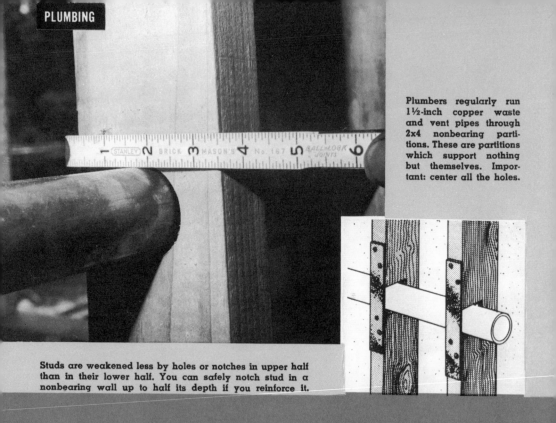

Plumbers regularly run 1½-inch copper waste and vent pipes through 2x4 nonbearing partitions. These are partitions which support nothing but themselves. Important: center all the holes.

Studs are weakened less by holes or notches in upper half than in their lower half. You can safely notch stud in a nonbearing wall up to half its depth if you reinforce it.

THINGS YOU SHOULD KNOW ABOUT . . .
cutting studs and joists

IF YOU PLAN to conceal plumbing pipes inside walls and floors, you'll have to cut studs and joists to do it. Joists are the horizontal members which support floors. Studs are the vertical framing members inside walls. Since any cutting of these members may weaken the house, it is important that such cutting be kept to a safe minimum.

How to Avoid Cutting. Water pipes are so small in size, they never present any problems in concealment. Big drainage pipes, however, do. In remodeling, when possible, instead of trying to conceal drainage pipes, run them up outside the walls and box them in.

A good method is to locate pipes in a corner. A jog in the wall, or closing in a small triangular space at a corner is scarcely noticeable, even if it includes a stack. The toilet itself may be set cater-corner against this new wall.

Where large drainage pipes run horizontally, if placed just outside the wall at ceiling level, they can be boxed in inconspicuously. Other horizontal drain pipes can be concealed by cabinet work, as in a vanity lavatory, or in a cabinet for linen and bath necessities.

If you are building an addition, by spacing joists to accommodate your plumbing, you can largely avoid cutting of these members. Never place a joist directly under a wet wall (a wall containing plumbing). Instead, place two spaced joists under it, just far enough apart to allow a 3- or 4-inch stack to be run up between them.

Avoid cutting joists by running pipes between them instead of across them. When possible, run pipes below joists in basement or crawl space, or above joists in an unfinished attic.

Often you can avoid cutting joists, or minimize the amount of cutting, by making use of the space occupied by flooring and subflooring, and laying a new floor over stripping, as shown.

You can safely run a 1½-inch pipe through any 2x8 joist if you center the hole between top and bottom. You may have to use a bend fitting to bring branch waste line off at the right level.

A cut through joist weakens it far less at the top than at the bottom. When a severe cut, like that shown, is necessary, keep the cut as close as possible to the top and reinforce the joist.

Plan placement of cuts carefully before you make them. The hole cut for branch waste pipe had to be shifted twice because of miscalculations. A cross member to adjoining joist adds support.

When a pipe has to cross joists, try to locate required notching as close as you can to point at which joists are supported. The deep notching, photo above, hardly weakens the joists at all.

Cutting Through Joists. You can safely bore a hole anywhere in a joist if it is centered between top and bottom and is not over ¼ the height of the joist at the location of the hole.

You can safely notch joists at either top or bottom, but only in the end quarters. FHA regulations permit notching in the end thirds of joists.

Don't notch a joist more than ⅙ its depth, except that you can notch it ⅓ its depth at the top, if the notching is no farther from the face of support than the depth of the joist. For example, on a 2x8 joist, notching would have to be within 7½ inches of the face of the joist's support. You're safe if you don't notch a joist more than ¼ the depth of the joist at its point of bearing. The depth of the joist here is often less than its depth elsewhere.

Always remember that the depth to which a joist may be safely cut decreases very rapidly as you move away from its point of support. Excessive cutting of joists will result in sagging, shaky floors, cracking and falling of ceiling plaster, and, in extreme cases, collapse of the structure. When a floor sags, it may interfere with drainage, for it may rob a drain pipe of its pitch, or even make it pitch in the wrong direction.

The one thing for which a joist may be cut completely through is to accommodate a closet bend. No more than one joist should be cut, however, and the cut end should be braced substantially.

Cutting Studs. According to new FHA minimum standards, unless reinforced with steel plates or furring across the notch, wall studs should never be notched more than ¼ their depth, nor should a hole bigger than 1¼ inches be cut or drilled in a 2x4 stud, or bigger than 2 inches in a 2x6 stud.

These regulations are somewhat stiffer than the general practice among plumbers. Their standard practice has been to notch

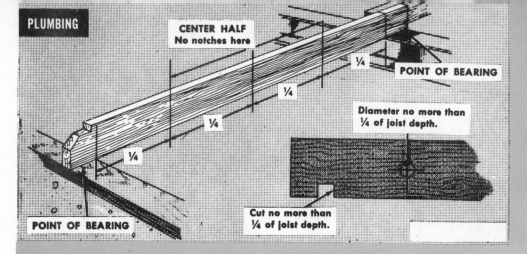

CENTER HALF No notches here

¼

¼

¼

¼

¼

POINT OF BEARING

Diameter no more than ¼ of joist depth.

Cut no more than ¼ of joist depth.

POINT OF BEARING

Don't notch a joist at all in the center section. The closer you are to the point of bearing, the deeper you can safely notch a joist. Notches made in joist's bottom edge will weaken it the most.

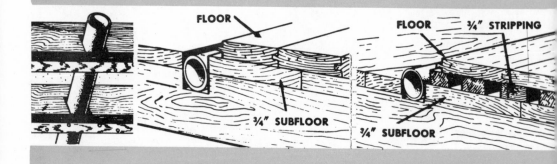

FLOOR

¾" SUBFLOOR

FLOOR   ¾" STRIPPING

¾" SUBFLOOR

Sears, Roebuck

Reinforce joist, left sketch, over or under notch with a 2x2 or steel strap. Then reduce notching of joists, center and right, to minimum by using space where flooring and subflooring is, or by using stripping.

the lower half of a stud up to ⅓ its depth without reinforcing. This permits them to run 1½-inch branch drains through 2x4 nonbearing partition walls.

Plumbers will notch a stud up to half its depth in its upper half without reinforcing if the partition is nonbearing. But they won't cut two studs in succession in this manner, or leave less than two uncut studs in a partition unless the cut studs are reinforced.

In no case does a competent plumber notch a stud over ⅔ its depth, for such a stud is worthless. It's impossible to reinforce it adequately.

Plan Ahead. Don't permit yourself to make mistakes. They will result in your cutting studs or joists, and then cutting them again to correct the original place-

ment of holes or notches. This is unnecessary weakening of the house structure. Carefully consider every cut before you make it to be sure it is absolutely necessary and that it will be exactly where you want it.

In arranging bathroom fixtures, plan their placement to minimize cutting. A lavatory placed on a wall opposite the toilet may require far more cutting of joists than one placed on the same wall as the toilet. Consider the direction in which joists run, and place fixtures so that pipes can run between joists rather than across them. If you do have to cut joists, always remember it is far better to do it near their ends. Never cut a joist in its center half.

Often, how much you can cut a member is just a matter of common sense. If its ob-

Running pipes through holes in center of joists is good system, but you may not have clearance for getting the pipes through the holes unless you plan ahead; install plumbing as you build.

This may look like severe cut, but actually the member cut isn't supporting anything at this particular point. On right and left, where it supports joists, member has adequate support underneath.

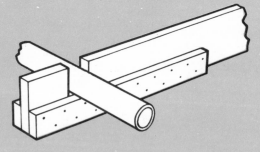

It takes only a little time to nail a length of 2-inch lumber to each side of the joist under a notch. It gives the joist important reinforcement where it is most needed—along bottom edge.

These two holes cut in floor are for the plumbing of two bathtubs placed back to back. Since the floor is a non-structural member, large cuts like this can be made wherever you require them.

vious that you are cutting away a main support, stop. The size of the member isn't always a sure indication of its importance. If you do have to cut away a main support, can you brace it as strongly as before by a reinforcing member placed close by? If so, put in the reinforcement before you make the cut.

Consider how substantially the house is built. If joists are on 12-inch centers where joists normally would be on 16-inch centers, you obviously can be a little more liberal in your notching. On the other hand, if the floor has 8-inch joists and really should have 10-inchers, go easy. If a floor already shakes when you walk across it, think what might happen if you weakened it. A cross beam, and a couple of lally columns to reduce span of joists will help. •

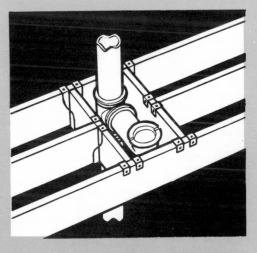

It is sometimes permissible to cut one joist to permit installation of a closet bend. When this is done, support the cut ends of joists securely. Use metal joist stirrups for maximum strength.

Glissade, Inc.

When you replace outmoded fixtures with attractive new ones beauty is added as well as value to your home. Lavatory vanity comes as a complete unit, with the basins and faucets already in proper place.

HOW TO INSTALL . . .

new fixtures

FIXTURES ARE INSTALLED after roughing-in of plumbing for them is complete. The roughed-in plumbing includes drainage and water-supply pipes.

Where an entire bathroom is being installed, the tub is the first fixture put in place. It is connected before the walls are finished. After finishing of the walls, toilet and lavatories are installed.

Care of Fixtures. Uncrate new fixtures carefully. Most damage to fixtures is done in unpacking them. Don't pry or hammer against a fixture in getting a crate off. Opened properly, crates usually unfold easily.

When you remove the crate, place the fixture on a blanket, or on excelsior pads and packing taken from the crate. If you have to slide a bathtub, place it on blocks of wood first. You can chip the edges on a fixture by sliding it on a rough floor or forcing it against a wall.

Once fixtures are damaged by scratching, or by being struck by tools, there is little that can be done about it. Cover fixtures to protect them. Cover bathtubs with a thick pad made of newspapers and wheat paste. It is a better covering than brush-on plastic types. Children can pick loose the plastic at a corner and rip the entire cover off.

Installing new fixtures is very simple. In addition, so many people are doing it that the necessary tubing and fittings for the job are now being sold in just about every well-stocked hardware, plumbing store.

The bathtub is the first fixture to be installed. The bathtub flange goes snugly against the wall studs. If you are remodeling, then it will be necessary to remove part of wall finish.

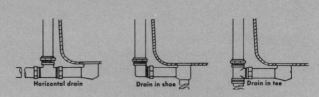

Diagrams above are of the tub's drain which can be hooked up to your plumbing in various ways. The bath drain can be ordered with the drain in a shoe, a drain in a tee, or it can be used as a horizontal drain (diagram at the left).

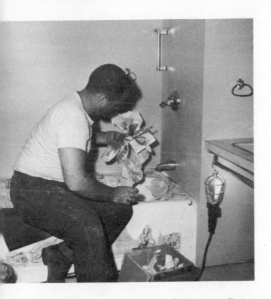

Protect tub against damage during installation. Cover it with newspaper applied with wheat paste.

Further, a plastic cover doesn't protect against the impact of dropped tools. You can buy paper covers, but what is the point of it when old newspapers make a superior cushion? Since wheat paste is soluble in water, soaking the paper makes it easy to remove after the job is complete.

Get the tub covering on right away. If the bathroom is to be tiled—and there is no better finish for bathroom walls than ceramic tile—the muriatic acid sometimes used in cleaning tile can mar the fixture's finish. Never stand in a bathtub, if you can avoid it, even when you do have it covered.

Wrap masking tape around the ends of roughed-in pipes. Plasterers will otherwise remove the caps on the pipe ends and plaster will get on the threads. Tape also protects fittings, specifically the spindles on which handles fit.

The end of a closet bend, after installation, should be closed to keep out debris during construction. An easy way to do it is to nail boards across the floor flange that's soldered to the bend. Another

Most lavatories are supported by hangers attached to wall. For solid support, use a 1x4 board recessed in studs at the required height.

Lavatory height may be varied from 29 to 36 inches, depending on whether fixture is to be used by children. Hangers are for a china lavatory.

method is to cut out a wooden plug of the appropriate size to fill the flange opening.

Installing a Tub. Most tubs are designed to fill completely a space between three walls. In remodeling, if a tub doesn't quite fill the existing space, build out one wall so it does. If the built-out space is large enough, you can use it for a built-in cabinet. When a tub is set against an outside wall, be certain the wall is insulated. Bathing comfort will suffer if it isn't.

Tub installation differs slightly according to the kind of tub and its manufacturer. Some tubs are installed on hangers nailed to studs. These metal devices help level the tub and also contribute toward eliminating the cracks and openings which frequently develop when such a support is not used. A mastic filler may be used between tub and hanger to make a waterproof seal.

In the installation of the typical steel tub, 1x4-inch boards are nailed to wall studs at

A counter style lavatory doesn't need hangers, special clamping ring is used. The trap is connected first (above) then the water supply tubes.

Here is a diagram of a typical trap and the relationship of the individual parts, e.g. value to the pipes, to flange, etc., and to the drainage line.

Below is detailed diagram for setting the hookup of supply piping from existing wall plumbing that is directly behind the wall onto the lavatory.

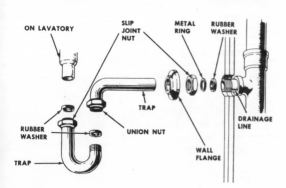

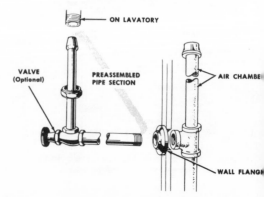

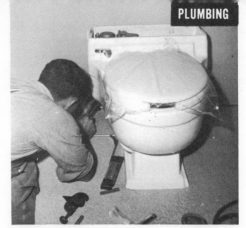

Toilet is connected to bolts set in slots of a floor flange. Blocks under flange are made so face is flush with floor. Plug keeps out debris.

Caulk outer rim of toilet bowl to make watertight seal. Wax ring is used for seal at drain. Position bowl on flange, twist slightly to seat it.

exactly the right height to support tub flanges when the tub is resting on the floor. The tub is anchored to the boards with screws through flange holes. Before this is done, a check is made to verify that the floor of the tub slopes toward the drain. Otherwise the tub won't empty properly. Some tubs employ a base strip as flashing to prevent water from infiltrating under the fixture.

It is necessary to have an access panel behind the tub, so that plumbing can be reached for servicing. The panel can be in an adjoining room or in an adjacent closet.

The tub branch drain and trap will already be in place. All that is necessary now is to connect the fixture's drain to the drain pipe end in the floor behind the tub. It is connected by means of a slip-joint nut, just like that on a lavatory. Supply line connections are also very similar to lavatory supply connections.

Grab bars are an absolute essential for safe use of tub or shower. Plan for them before applying finish to walls, so that you can add studs or cross-braces into which the grab bars can later be screwed. These bars may have to withstand a pull of 300 pounds or more so just fastening them into plaster isn't likely to be sufficient. Keep a record of where studs or reinforcements are. They may be difficult to locate exactly after the wall finish is on.

Place an "L" or vertical bar 24 inches from the shower end of the tub, with the bottom of the "L" 26 inches from the floor.

Installing a Toilet. A toilet should have a minimum clearance at its front of 18 inches. No wall or opposite fixture should be closer than this. No wall should be closer to the sides of the bowl than 15 inches, measuring from the bowl's center line.

Some toilets combine the tank and bowl in a single piece, others have a separate

One-piece toilets, like the one in the center drawing, have tank and bowl as a single unit, so that no assembly is required. A water supply connection is similar to that for basin, as sketched on left, but special toilet supply tubes are used. At right, is connection to floor employing straight and not angle valve.

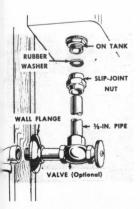

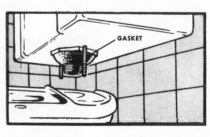

tank and bowl. Roughed-in plumbing will have provided a floor flange. Two bolts come up through this flange, and the toilet fastens to them. If the toilet requires 4 bolts, the 2 extra bolts go into the bowl's front holes and are screwed into the floor. Use special toilet-bowl bolts. These have wood threads at one end, machine threads at the other. If the floor is concrete, use regular machine bolts set head down into holes and fill around them with mortar.

With the bowl upside down on a protective pad or blanket, make a putty ring about 1 inch high around the outside rim of the bottom. Place a wax ring around the discharge opening. If the floor level is above the top of the flange you will have to double the ring. Now carefully set the toilet down on the flange bolts, twisting the bowl slightly to spread the putty and wax and make a tight seal.

If the toilet has a separate tank, you'll probably find that it is held by two bolts and that a "flush ell" is provided to make the connection between tank and bowl. If the tank rests on the bowl, a gasket will make a tight seal as the two units are bolted together. Water supply connections can be made with Plumb Shop tubes. Get the 12-inch size for connection to the wall, a 20-inch size for one to the floor.

A new type of toilet is wall-hung. These come in several different styles, but typically are supported by a heavy hanger bolted to the wall studs on the inside of the wall. The discharge end of the toilet fits into the soil pipe, which is part of the hanger assembly, and makes a watertight fit by means of a gasket.

Don't overlook the need for a tissue holder when planning your toilet installation. Standard placement for this is 6 inches in front of the toilet and 26 inches from the floor, measuring to the holder's center. •

If pipes or wiring interfere with recessing of medicine cabinet, you can get surface units or fur out the walls to achieve the required depth.

To combine two or more cabinets into one unit, use joining strips, such as the ones supplied with the cabinets made by F. H. Lawson in this photograph.

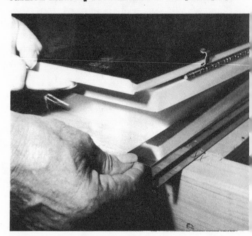

After test-fitting of cabinets into the frame, nail securely to the existing wall studs. All cabinets require a depth of 3½ inches recessing in frame.

Quality cabinets are bonderized to permanently protect screw holes against rust. Mirrors can be had in window glass or flawless plate glass.